A GEOCENTRICITY PRIMER

Introduction to Biblical Cosmology

by

Gerardus D. Bouw, Ph.D.

The Biblical Astronomer
Cleveland

Revised and corrected 2004

TABLE OF CONTENTS

> Accommodation: the theory which states that God goes along with the commonly accepted story even though he really doesn't believe it.
>
> — Anonymous

PREFACE

Four hundred years ago there raged a debate among the learned men of Europe about whether or not the earth orbits the sun. Until then, it was commonly accepted that the sun, moon, stars, and planets were embedded in crystalline spheres centered on the earth. In the debate, the Biblicists held that the sun goes around the earth once a day as well as once a year; whereas, the secularists maintained that the earth daily rotates on an axis and orbits the sun once a year. This latter idea, called heliocentrism, held the sun to be at the center of the universe. The modern view is that there is no center to the universe.

When geocentrism (the idea that the earth is stationary at the center of the universe) was finally defeated, humanists heralded the victory as signifying the death of the Bible and, consequently, the death of Christianity as a reasonable faith. Many who contributed to the defeat of the Bible's authority on nature were names now famous. Most notable are Copernicus, Kepler, and Galileo. However, the victory was not total, for there have been supporters of geocentrism until this very day. Among the most famous and capable of the early geocentric defenders are Tycho Brahe and three generations of the Parisian astronomers, Cassini.

In the last half of the twentieth century, geocentrism resurfaced in a new, technical form called *geocentricity*. Among its advocates and supporters one finds several with earned Ph.D.s in astronomy, mathematics or physics. Two world-wide organizations serve the geocentric community. One is the Association for Biblical Astronomy (A.B.A., formerly called the Tychonian Society), and the other is the *Cercle Scientifique et Historique* (CESHE) which maintains offices in Belgium and France. Differences in whether or not the earth rotates and the size of the universe is what distinguishes the two groups. CESHE is devoutly Roman Catholic and was organized to promote the works of Fr. Fernand Crombette, believes in a small universe with rotating earth; A.B.A., which holds the Holy Bible as its final authority, takes the opposite position.

Now the typical reader may be puzzled by such a resurgence of an old, "long-dead" idea. After all, what are the issues? The essential argument is presented by the chapter quote. At issue is the inerrancy and preservation of Scripture, especially in the light of the pronouncements of science. At stake is the authority of the Bible in all realms, starting in the realm of science.

So, is geocentricity an anti-scientific myth? Is it actually a throw-back to the flat earth? Is it the case, as one creationist group claims, that geocentrists are heretics teaching an end-time heresy? Or is there something to geocentricity, after all? And what does it have to do with Mach's Principle, which makes geocentricity as plausible as any other center? Such questions constitute the substance of this book. But until all the issues are aired out in the open, geocentrists will just have to stick to Acts 24:14:

> But this I confess unto thee, that after the way which they call heresy, so worship I the God of my fathers, believing *all* things which are written in the law and in the prophets. [Emphasis added.]

My special thanks to the many people who have spurred me on with the writing of this book by their expressions of encouragement and interest. In particular, I wish to thank my wife, Beth, for her support, and Prof. James Hanson for his encouragement and contributions in its writing, and for Gordon Bane for publishing this abridged edition.

Cleveland, Ohio, 8 November 2004

Yea, hath God said...?
— Satan, Genesis 3:1

1

THE SIGNIFICANCE

To hear tell, geocentrism, the ancient doctrine that the earth is fixed motionless at the center of the universe, died over four centuries ago. At that time Nicolaus Copernicus, a Polish canon who earned his living by preparing astrological charts for his mentor, claimed that the sun and not the earth was at the center of the universe. His idea is known as *heliocentrism*. Despite the best efforts of vocal and enthusiastic supporters such as Galileo Galilei, it took almost a hundred years for heliocentrism to become the dominant opinion; and it did so without any scientific evidence in its favor.

The Copernican Revolution, as this change of view is called, was not just a revolution in astronomy, but it also spread into politics and theology. In particular, it set the stage for the development of Bible criticism. After all, if God cannot be taken literally when he writes of the "rising of the sun," then how can he be taken literally in writing of the "rising of the Son?"

By contrast, there was *geocentrism,* the ancient belief that the earth is located at the center of the universe. Until well into the seventeenth century the thought that the earth was immobile at the center of the universe was taken for granted to be both Biblical and natural. The earth was, after all, central in God's attention, affection, and purpose. It was to the earth that Jesus Christ came. It was on earth that he died; and it was on earth that he was resurrected for the sins of *man,* not any other creature of the cosmos. It is on earth that those things which "the angels desire to look into" (1 Peter 1:12) are occurring. How logical, then, the idea that the earth is nestled unmoving at the center of all creation?

But the rise of *heliocentrism* in the sixteenth century changed all that. Gradually the heliocentric belief became the dominant belief so that today, except for minor modifications, one is considered scientifically illiterate if one seriously questions heliocentrism at all. Actually, modern science no longer believes the Copernican and Galilean idea that the sun is at the center of the universe. Today's predominant scientific opinion has it that there is no center to the universe. So the modern view is more properly termed *acentrism,* but because of its widespread historical familiarity we will refer to the modern point of view as *heliocentrism* throughout this work.

That the Bible is overtly geocentric has been noted by believer and unbeliever alike. Augustus De Morgan, an agnostic and one of the foremost mathematicians of the nineteenth century, wrote about the immobility of the earth as taught in the Bible:

> The question of the earth's motion was the single point in which orthodoxy came into real contact with science. Many students of physics were suspected of magic, many of atheism: but, stupid as the mistake may have been, it was *bona fide* the magic or the atheism, not the physics, which was assailed. In the astronomical case it was the very doctrine, as doctrine, independently of consequences, which was the *corpus delicti*: and this because it contradicted the Bible. And so it did; for the stability of the earth is as clearly assumed from one end of the Old Testament to the other as the solidity of iron. Those who take the Bible to be *totidem verbis* dictated by the God of Truth can refuse to believe it; and they make strange reasons. They undertake, *a priori*, to settle Divine intentions. The Holy Spirit did not *mean* to teach natural philosophy: this they know beforehand; or else they infer it from finding out that the earth does move, and the Bible says it does not. Of course, ignorance apart, every word is truth, or the writer did not mean truth. But this puts the whole book on its trial: for we can never find out what the writer meant, unless we otherwise find out what is true. Those who like may, of course, declare for an inspiration over which they are to be viceroys;

but common sense will either accept the verbal meaning or deny verbal inspiration.[1]

Likewise, the famous twentieth-century agnostic philosopher, Bertrand Russell, recognized the crucial challenge which heliocentrism presented to the Bible's authority when he wrote of the Ten Commandments that their authority:

> rests upon the authority of the Bible, which can only be maintained intact if the Bible is accepted as a whole. When the Bible seems to say that the earth does not move, we must adhere to this statement in spite of the arguments of Galileo, since otherwise we shall be giving encouragement to murderers and all other kinds of malefactors. Although few would now accept this argument, it cannot be regarded as absurd, nor should those who acted upon it be viewed with moral reprobation.[2]

Several pages later, Bertrand Russell writes about the demise of geocentrism concomitant with the Bible's authority among Christians. He notes that:

> . . . inconvenient Bible texts were interpreted allegorically or figuratively.[3]

and, still later he credits the Copernican Revolution with the demise of Christians themselves as authorities:

> . . . in the period of time since Copernicus, whenever science and theology have disagreed, science has proved victorious.[4]

It is not just the philosophers and mathematicians but also theologians who recognize and admit the inherent geocentricity of the Bible. Rabbi Louis Jacobs of London, for example, while writing of the biblical model of the universe, states that "the Biblical picture is clearly geocentric."[5] In rare moments of candor, even

Evangelical theologians will also reflect on the problem of reconciling the geocentricity of the Bible with the heliocentrism of modern science:

> To illustrate what we mean by unconvincing hermeneutical procedures, we need only recall the way many conservatives seek to harmonize the Bible with the Copernican view of the universe. When Copernicus first abandoned the geocentric model of the universe for a heliocentric one, the church was appalled. Church leaders appealed to Scripture, which compares the sun to "a strong man running a race whose circuit is from one end of heaven to the other" (Psalm 19:4 and 5) and which declares that the "world also is established that it cannot be moved" (Psalm 93:1). From these and similar texts they conclude that the sun moves around the earth which remains fixed in its position. They were correct insofar as this is what the text of the Scripture says. Today, however, we can no longer accept this as a scientific description of what happens. Some conservatives, however, feel compelled to reconcile Scripture with reality. Normally they handle the problem by replying that the passages in the Psalms are poetry. But this hermeneutical observation is more erudite than helpful, for poetry is as clear in its meaning as prose. "The world also is established that it cannot be moved" can hardly be a poetic way of saying that the earth is spinning on its axis and gyrating through space in a path determined by the orbit of the sun. The meaning which the older interpreters gave the text is no doubt the meaning the author intended. To admit as much is simply to apply the fundamental hermeneutical canon of the grammatical-historical method.[6]

From these several quotations it becomes evident just what the central issue is in the heliocentric debate: the issue is that of the authority of the Holy Bible. Did God really write "true truth," as Francis Schaeffer called it; or did he write an untruth for the sake of convenience so that his word would not appear too cryptic to the ancient mind? However, this begs the question of why God would make it cryptic for us and not for the ancients. Is the Bible clear in its teachings, or do we need scientific "experts" to advise us as to what "God really *meant* to say" but evidently did not have the wits to say properly, forthrightly or plainly? And if God does write things which are not true truth in those passages which refer to the immobility of the earth, then how can man trust anything else God writes? How could we possibly know what God "meant" to say or what is true if he does not say what he means in the first place? Or is the heliocentric idea merely another version of Satan's ploy to deceive Eve as recorded in Genesis 3:1, to cast doubt upon the veracity of God's word? And finally, is the evidence for heliocentrism really as overwhelming as the elementary text books make it seem, or is this one of those cases which Kuhn refers to when he writes of the origins and history of scientific ideas that:

> In the case of textbooks, at least, there are even good reasons why, in these matters, they should be systematically misleading.[7]

Finally, over the last century, there has been an explosion of knowledge, unprecedented in history, in the light of which geocentrism has returned in a new form called *geocentricity*. The key distinction between geocentricity and geocentrism is this: geocentrism was, as the suffix *-ism* relates, a divisive idea; divisive in the sense that the model did not allow for a universe in which the parts were free to interact. Before and throughout the Dark Ages, the geocentric model was one where the planets moved on crystalline spheres and where no astral body could leave its particular sphere. Geocentricity, by contrast, is an integrative model which ties the parts of the cosmos together into a whole. Heliocentrism, on the other hand, generally needs additional hypotheses for its explanation of a phenomenon. This aspect of geocentricity we shall examine in the last chapters of the book. But first, we examine the biblical model.

Wherefore, if meat make my brother to offend, I will eat no flesh while the world standeth, lest I make my brother to offend.

— 1 Corinthians 8:13

2

MOTIONS OF THE WORLD

The Bible makes a consistent and important distinction between the world and the earth. It is crucial that this distinction be understood in looking at the motions of the earth and world in scripture. Literally, the word *world* comes from two Germanic roots: *wer*, meaning "man," and *ald*, meaning "age" or "old." Job 37:12 best serves to illustrate the difference between the words "earth" and "world" when it states:

And [God's bright cloud] is turned round by his counsels: that [God's clouds] may do whatsoever he commandeth them upon the face of the world in the earth.

The clause "upon the face of the world in the earth" indicates that if it can be shown that the world does not move, that then the earth does not move either, and *vice versa*. So we must look at the moving and fixed-world passages to see if they are consistent with the motions ascribed to the earth in the Bible.

The Bible references to the immobility of the world can be broken up into two groups: the first group is those which refer to the world to come, while the other group refers to this present world. That these two worlds are not one and the same is clearly presented in Matthew 12:32 where Jesus rebukes those who blaspheme against the Holy Ghost with the words:

...it shall not be forgiven...neither in this world, neither in the world to come.

It is the latter world that is sometimes referred to as the "world without end" in such places as Isaiah 45:17 and Ephesians 3:21. When it comes to this present world, there are only two references in the entire Bible describing its motion.

Motions of the Present World – Psalm 93:1

The first of the two references to the motion of this present world occurs in Psalm 93:1 which reads, in part:

. . . the world also is stablished, that it cannot be moved.

The word "stablished" may sound strange to the modern ear, but it communicates a very subtle point which, though present in the Hebrew, is lacking in all modern versions which favor the word "establish," instead. *Stablish* means to stabilize; *establish* means to set up. The rendering in the King James Bible reflects God's continuing, stabilizing influence on this present world. This makes a lot of sense considering that the world is founded on waters (also compare Genesis 49:4). To use the English word "established" in this verse would allow one to draw the erroneous conclusion that God "set up" the present evil world system and now lets it run down on its own, analogous to the Mohammedan idea of *kismet*. By contrast, the use of the word *stablish* indicates that God is actively keeping the world from the destabilizing effects of evil. As if to underscore that theme, the next verse of Psalm 93 interjects God's throne into the picture. It is from the throne that righteousness will judge:

Thy throne is established of old: thou art from everlasting.

We shall have more to say on the matter when we talk about the earth as footstool to the throne.

Since Psalm 93:1 indicates that the world cannot be moved, it would follow that it is not now moving. Some heliocentric apologists have suggested that what the verse is *really* saying is that the earth can neither be deflected out of its orbit around the sun nor be perturbed in its orbit. They maintain that what God *really* means is that the **orbit** of the earth is stable rather than that the **world** is stablished. But is God really such a clumsy grammarian? If that is what God *really meant* to say, then could he not have done so simply by changing the wording a little? After all, what would be so unusual or cryptic about his having written words to the effect of "the circuit of the world"? God does so in Psalm 19:6, for example, where reference is made to the "circuit" of the sun. Or could he not better have written of the "course of the world" instead? Furthermore, proper grammar would have required that God then use such words as "deflected" or "perturbed" instead of "moved" if, indeed, the passage is intended to refer to the earth's motion through space.

Now there are two problems with the heliocentrists' interpretations. First, they have confused the world with the earth; and second, they have violated their own heliocentric physics. Consider: the interpretation brought to bear is that the earth cannot be deflected in its orbit. But every physics student knows that the earth is constantly being deflected, being subject to the gravitational influences of all of the other planets. So heliocentrically speaking, the earth is being deflected in its orbit. Even its very orbit is deflected, which deflection is called the *perihelion precession*.

It is interesting to look at some of the interpretations of Psalm 93:1 as conceived by various revisionists. Kenneth Taylor, for example, in his *Living Bible* (which Taylor claims is not a Bible yet he titled it a Bible anyhow), goes so far as to equate the "establishing" of the world with the "establishing" of God's throne in Psalm 93:2 and promptly declares that the world is God's throne. This is not only bad translating but also bad exegesis and logic as well. Isaiah 66:1 clearly teaches that the earth is God's footstool, not his throne; Psalm 11:4 places God's throne in heaven and not on earth.

Sometimes the revisionists' attempts around the implicit geocentricity of the passage humorously confounds them. De Witt, in his *Praise Songs of Israel* renders Psalm 93:1 as:

So the world standeth fast; it cannot be overthrown.

Changing "cannot be moved" to "cannot be overthrown" certainly does remove the geocentric overtones of the verse. But notice that "stablished" has been changed to "standeth fast" which reintroduces the geocentricity of the passage, by moving it to the previous phrase.

R. K. Harrison, in his *Psalms for Today*, has decided that the word "world" is not proper English because of the geocentricity inherent in the passage. Instead of what is properly translated as "world," he opts for a more obscure and archaic meaning for "world," namely, "universe." If "universe" is actually meant here instead of "world" then this would be the only such occurrence in Scripture. To assume this on the say-so of heliocentrists is sheer folly. Harrison renders the verse as:

The universe has been established immovably.

So we see that attempts to circumvent the geocentricity inherent in Psalm 93:1 have proven to be rather weak, even comical.

Motions of the Present World – 1 Corinthians 8:13

The second of the two passages which speak of the lack of motion on the part of the world is 1 Corinthians 8:13:

Wherefore, if meat make my brother to offend, I will eat no flesh while the world standeth, lest I make my brother to offend.

Since only the Authorized Bible renders this verse in a geocentric context, it might be objected that this is just bad translating on the part of King James's translating committee. But there is more involved than simply that. Psalm 12:6-7,[1] in all Reformation translations as well as the old Hebrew lexicons, indicates that the word of God will be inerrantly translated and preserved into every language. All modern versions as well as the Reformation translations read "forever" instead of "while the world standeth" in 1 Corinthians 8:13. Despite this, the Greek idiom is phrased exactly as we find it in the Authorized Translation. Furthermore, that rendering is consistent with the translators' resolve to use the same English wording for each Greek wording wherever the context allowed it.

In summary, then, there are no passages which indicate any motion for this present world; and two verses, Psalm 93:1 and 1 Corinthians 8:13, expressly deny any motion is partaken of by this current world.

Motions of the World to Come

If no motion is experienced by this present world, then certainly none should be experienced in the perfect world to come. Here, too, we find only two verses with reference to the new world's motion. These are 1 Chronicles 16:30 and Psalm 96:10. I Chronicles 16:30 reads:

Fear before him, all the earth: the world also shall be stable, that it be not moved.

The word "shall" here indicates the future tense so that, by itself, the verse cannot be invoked to indicate that the present world is immobile. But it does teach that the world to come will be stable and unmoving.

Again, the suggestion has been made by heliocentrists that the verse refers to the orbit of the new earth; but the same arguments as were presented against that interpretation of Psalm 93:1 can be invoked against using that interpretation here. To indicate heliocentrism, the Masoretic text and all the translations should have used "deflected" or "perturbed" instead of "moved."

Interestingly, some heliocentrists have totally missed that this verse is in the future tense, and have attacked its validity on the erroneous assumption that the **present world** is here claimed to be immovable.

Psalm 96:10, the second passage about the immobility of the world to come, reads:

> Say among the heathen, that the LORD reigneth: the world also shall be established that it shall not be moved: he shall judge the people righteously.

This verse is strongly reminiscent of Psalm 93:1. Note here that the word "established" is used whereas in the former verse the word "stablished" was used. In the light of what we noted earlier in this chapter about the distinction between these two words, the use of "established" here shows that the world to come will be "set up" by the LORD without any process of decay; and that, as such, it will not contain the evil that is inherent in this present world. This conclusion, too, is absolutely Biblical.

Conclusion

In summary, then, there is not one single passage in the entire 66 books of the Bible which would lead one to conclude that the world is now or ever will be moving. Instead, we found one reference which directly indicates that this present world is not moving, and two verses which say that the world to come will not move either. Attempts to reconcile these verses with modern heliocentrism make God out to be a clumsy grammarian and make the reconcilers out to be the clairvoyants of what God actually *meant* to say but did not care to say clearly in the first place.

But if the world does not move, then what of the earth? Let us look at those verses next.

Sanctify them through thy truth: thy word is truth.

— John 17:17

3

MOTIONS OF THE EARTH

Like the biblical passages which deal with the motions of the world, the passages which refer to the motions of the earth can be divided into two categories. But unlike the "world" passages, there are no "moving earth" references to a "new earth." Instead, the earth passages can be split into those which pertain to the earth as it now is and those which describe the condition of the earth at the last judgment.

Motions of this Present Earth — Psalm 104:5

The most famous and yet among the weakest of all geocentric passages is Psalm 104:5, which states that God:

> ...laid the foundations of the earth, that it should not be removed for ever.

Heliocentrists have assailed this verse from a number of different angles; yet strangely, none seem ever to have correctly read the verse. Psalm 104:5 is conditional: it is not absolute; for we see the conditional "should" which does not necessarily reflect the way things are. Heliocentrists, having missed that point, have charged that the words "laid the foundations" are improperly translated from the Hebrew; or they claim that the word "removed" is not correct; or they dismiss it as mere poetry, as if poetry never conveys literal truth. One of these charges we have already addressed in the first chapter. The long quote from De Morgan lucidly denotes the logical flaw in the "phenomenological poetry" argument—

every word is true, poetry or prose, or the God of Truth could not have written it. With this, the chapter quote concurs.

What of the first of the charges, the one about the correctness of the "laid the foundations" translation? The critics prefer "set the earth on its foundations." But this does not in the least affect the implicit geocentricity of the verse. Instead, such an argument introduces an uncertainty about just who, then, "laid the foundations" if God only "set" the earth upon them. As far as the translation is concerned, the correct translation is "laid the foundations" even as we find it in the Authorized King James Bible.

In looking at the second of the arguments, the status of the word "removed," it is advisable to consult a dictionary. In previous chapters we have noted several cases where so-called archaic or "difficult" words have revealed very subtle shades of meaning, shades which are generally lost on Bible critics. The word "removed" affords us such an example. "Removed" means "to shift out of a designated place." "Move," on the other hand, means to change position. Thus "removed" indicates that the earth is located in a place which is special to it: a place especially prepared for it, a "home" for it. In fact, the British still use the word "remove" when a family moves from one dwelling to another. This subtle overtone is also present in the Hebrew and so is exactly translated by the use of the word "remove." Hence there is no problem with the translation of Psalm 104:5.

In Psalm 104:5, too, it has been proposed that the verse *really* refers to the orbit of the earth, indicating that the orbit is stable and that the earth shall not be "removed" or "moved" out of it. This raises the same objections that we saw in Chapter 2 where that proposal was applied to Psalm 93:1. Again, should God then not have written "deflected" or "perturbed from its course" instead of "removed"? Actually, according to modern astronomy the earth is continually being perturbed in its orbit by the gravitational pull of the other planets in their respective orbits about the sun. Thus the proposal that the verse refers to the orbit of the earth does not at all bring the text into "conformity" with modern science. There is simply no heliocentric view which is compatible with any of the various attempts around this passage, let alone with the literal truth of it.

Some of the Reformation translations are even stronger in their geocentric import of this verse than is the Authorized Bible. The Dutch *Statenbijbel*, for example, reads "totter" instead of "removed." Some modern versions also use that word; but in so doing the heliocentrists strongly bring themselves into direct conflict with modern astronomy because, according to astronomy, the earth is perpetually tottering on its axis, a phenomenon known as the *precession of the equinoxes*. The precession of the equinoxes is exactly akin to the tottering of a top or gyroscope. (In the geocentric case the tottering is ascribed to the heavens, not to the earth; but more of that in our later consideration of the scientific evidence.) No matter what the heliocentrist tries, there seems to be no way around the conclusion that the verse is geocentric.

Psalm 104:5 is of such great historical importance in the debate between heliocentrism and geocentricity that private interpretations and attempts at phenomenalization abound. Let us examine just a few of these as representative of all. We start off with De Witt who, in his *Praise Songs of Israel* presents:

... that it should not be overthrown for ever.

Verkuyl, in his *Modern Language* The New Berkeley Version in modern English, (ML) agrees, rendering it as:

... so that it should never be overthrown.

Taylor's *Living Bible* (LB) gives the verse as:

... that it should never fall apart.

The *New King James* (NKJV) loses the fine points of the verse with its rendition of:

... so that it should not be moved for ever.

Finally, the *Revised Standard Version* (RSV) offers us:

... so that it should never be shaken.

Quickly let us note that contrary to the RSV, the earth does "shake" during an earthquake; and despite the LB, it will "fall apart" at the end time. At that same time, Isaiah 24:19-20 say that it will be "overthrown"; contrary to De Witt and Verkuyl. We could go on and on and round and round with this; but as was noted, the heliocentrist has completely missed the one "out" afforded him.

Despite the long, hot debate about Psalm 104:5, most of it has been in vain. The resolution of the text does not hinge upon whether or not the earth be "moved" or "removed." Nor does it hinge on whether or not it is the earth that is referred to in this verse or else its orbit around the sun. The simple fact is that the verse is conditional. Despite the centuries of arguing, the verse neither proves nor disproves geocentricity. All that Psalm 104:5 says is that God "...laid the foundations of the earth, that it *should* not be removed for ever." The word, should, is a conditional word, a word which must not be held to necessarily reflect things as they are.

In short, the text does not say that God laid the foundations of the earth that *it not be* removed for ever. The verse teaches neither geocentricity nor heliocentrism − it merely states that the earth was founded in such a way that it "should not be removed for ever." If an inference must be drawn, however, it is clear that the inference is geocentric.

The Abiding Earth

There are two other verses in the Bible which verses seem to indicate the immobility of the earth. The first of these is Psalm 119:90 which states that:

Thy faithfulness is unto all generations: thou hast established the earth, and it abideth.

The second such passage is found in Ecclesiastes 1:4:

One generation passeth away, and another generation cometh: but the earth abideth for ever.

Both of these verses use the word "abide," a word which in English is not particularly strong in indicating a stationary earth. Historically, however, both verses have been held to support geocentricity. Interestingly, most of this has been done by Jewish scholars rather than Christian scholars. This is because the geocentric implication of these verses is much stronger in Hebrew than in English. Note that in both Hebrew and English the word "abide" has in it not only the sense of waiting, but also a sense of dwelling, which is consistent with the earlier discussion about the word "removed" in Psalm 104:5.

From all the passages of Scripture to which we have turned thus far no strong case can be built in support of geocentricity, but there is certainly no support for heliocentrism there either. By contrast, there is a set of Bible passages which do express definite motion on the part of the earth. These verses all refer to the earth in the context of the judgment. Yet these passages, although they afford the earth some motion, do not at all help the cause of heliocentrism.

The Moving Earth

There are actually several passages which refer to motions on the part of the earth. The first occurs in Job 9:6 which states that God:

shaketh the earth out of her place, and the pillars thereof tremble.

The second, Psalm 99:1, speaks likewise:

> The LORD reigneth; let the people tremble: he sitteth between the cherubims; let the earth be moved.

Isaiah 13:13 contibutes:

> Therefore I will shake the heavens, and the earth shall remove out of her place, in the wrath of the LORD of hosts, and in the day of his fierce anger.

Finally, Isaiah 24:19-20 is even broader:

> [19] The earth is utterly broken down, the earth is clean dissolved, the earth is moved exceedingly.
> [20] The earth shall reel to and fro like a drunkard, and shall be removed like a cottage; and the transgression thereof shall be heavy upon it; and it shall fall, and not rise again.

Notice that implicit in several of these verses is the notion that this present earth has a *place*, not a *path*. "Place" is hardly a fitting terminology for a moving earth in this context. Again, if a heliocentric context had been intended then would God not have better used such words as "course," "orbit," or "circuit" instead of "place"? Such wording is not mystical or obscure and is entirely consistent with heliocentrism. If the earth is to be shaken out of its place at the judgment, then at that time the earth definitely will have motion. This concept of a motion for the earth at the judgment time is entirely consistent with the rest of the scriptures and with all judgment passages which refer to the earth; it is only superficially inconsistent with verses such as Psalm 104:5 where the disallowance of motion is conditional.

Note that in Isaiah 13:13 the use of the word "remove" is fantastically consistent on the part of the Authorized Bible. As was noted earlier in this chapter, Psalm 104:5 teaches that the earth "should not be *removed*"; and we saw that the word "remove" has implicit in it the sense of the earth having a special place of its own. The word "move" has no such significance, yet here, in this verse, the earth's place is again in evidence. There is no contradiction between the earth's being removed, as per this passage, and the statement that it should never be removed in Psalm 104:5, because the latter is conditional. The Bible teaches that it is man's sin which causes the conditions to change so that the earth will ultimately be removed even though it was founded so that it should never be removed.

Psalm 99:1 does not necessarily say that the earth is now moving, it only says "*let* the earth be moved." It indicates the removal of something that is presently hindering the earth from moving. Hence this can not refer to changes in the course of the earth through space. It implies an earth that is presently immobile. (Strangely, if taken out of context this is the only verse in the Bible where one might remotely conclude that the earth is currently allowed to move; but heliocentrists fail to pick up on it, choosing instead to alter the wording to read "quiver," "shake," or "quake" instead of "move.")

As far as Isaiah 24:19-20 are concerned, again note the presence of the word "removed" in the immediate context of a dwelling (cottage). Remember, too, that the world, not earth, is said to be immovable in Psalm 93:1. We see the fulfillment of this thought in Revelation 20:11 where it says of the earth:

> And I saw a great white throne, and him that sat on it, from whose face the earth and the heaven fled away; and there was found no place for them.

They are replaced by a new heaven and a new earth. The transfer of the inhabitants amounts to a removal.

We might expect that if the earth is to move at the end times, that there might be some reference to the foundations of the earth to emphasize the fact of that motion. Psalm 82:5 does give us such a reference when it states that the wicked:

> know not, neither will they understand; they walk on in darkness: all the foundations of the earth are out of course.

The context of this passage, too, refers to the final judgment; for the Psalm begins with:

God standeth in the congregation of the mighty; he judgeth among the gods...

and it ends with:

Arise, O God, judge the earth: for thou shalt inherit all nations.

But what of the use of the phrase "out of course" here? Does this not indicate that the present earth has a course and is thus not standing still? May we not conclude this even though the verse refers to the judgment? Does this not contradict the other verses which indicate that the earth is not moving? We might indeed be able to draw this conclusion if it were not for the simple fact that this verse does not speak of the earth being out of course but instead speaks of the *foundations of the earth being out of course.*

When it comes to the earth's foundations, we need only consider two: the underlying foundation, which is the Lord Jesus Christ himself, and the core of the earth. The context of the Psalm is the judgment. Christ came to earth to atone for the sins of man and thus to enable the salvation of anyone and everyone who would believe his sacrifice to be both necessary and sufficient. On those who do so falls none of the last judgment. Having the sin of the entire world imputed him would most certainly be "out of course" for the Sinless One. Furthermore, in considering the nature of the earth's core, which is one of its "foundations," it is noted that there are fluid motions in the core of the earth. These motions maintain the magnetic field of the earth. Technically, for life to persist, the magnetic field should be relatively strong. There are a number of reasons for this, but the most important is that the magnetic field of the earth deflects cosmic rays (high-energy particles from space akin to radioactivity) which, among other damage, cause cancer. The earth's magnetic field is decaying at a rate that indicates it should vanish in one or two thousand years. This, too, when applied to the earth's core, could be viewed as a foundation "out of course."

Historically, no heliocentrist has ever gone on record favoring Psalm 82:5 as proof for a moving earth; and there is good reason for this. No argument on behalf of a moving earth can solidly be based upon this verse. The context is all too clearly that of the last judgment, just as is the case for all Bible references to a moving earth.

Conclusion

The end of the matter is this: the earth is not moving; it has a place of its own. But at the great white throne judgment, the earth will be removed; it will flee away and move for the first time in its history. After these events there will be a new heaven and a new earth; one which is perpetually sustained by the Lord in a way that this present world is not sustained; for that new world will have been bought by the precious blood of the Son of God.

And Hezekiah answered, it is a light thing
for the shadow to go down ten degrees.

— 2 Kings 20:10

4

HEZEKIAH'S SIGN

Three times, in three different places, the Bible tells the story of
Hezekiah's terminal illness, his appeal to God for recovery,
and God's gracious promise of recovery accompanied by a sign to
assure Hezekiah of the truth of God's promise. The heliocentrists,
in their attempts to reconcile the miracle with natural "laws," generally concentrate on only one of the three accounts. Let us begin
with 2 Kings 20:9-11:

> [9] And Isaiah said, This sign shalt thou have of the LORD,
> that the LORD will do the thing he hath spoken: shall the
> shadow go forward ten degrees, or go back ten degrees?
> [10] And Hezekiah answered, It is a light thing for the shadow
> to go down ten degrees: nay, but let the shadow return
> backward ten degrees.
> [11] And Isaiah the prophet cried unto the LORD: and he
> brought the shadow ten degrees backward, by which it had
> gone down in the dial of Ahaz.

Historically, Biblicists have interpreted this as indicating that the
sun backed up ten degrees in its daily path and then continued its
regular descent from that point on. That particular day would have
been forty minutes longer than a normal day. But not all agree that
such is the correct interpretation. Let us examine the evidence.

The Shadow Did It

Considering the above text by itself, it may be argued that
since only the *shadow* on the sundial ("dial") is mentioned, only

the shadow on the sundial went back and so the sun was not affected by the sign. That day was, then, a normal 24-hour day as far as the rest of the world was concerned. The sun itself did not change position in the sky; only the shadow went back. Effectively this makes the sign an "optical illusion" which could be witnessed only on the sundial which Hezekiah's father, Ahaz, had built. If this were all that the Bible says about the event then we would be justified in concluding just that.

Seen Only in Judah

But the 2 Kings account is not the only one in the Bible; we have another mention of the event in 2 Chronicles 32:24 which, though it adds no detail to the event, confirms its reality by saying:

> In those days Hezekiah was sick to death, and prayed unto the LORD: and he spake unto him, and gave him a sign.

After Hezekiah's recovery Berodach-baladan, king of Babylon, sent ambassadors to Hezekiah to inquire about the sign and Hezekiah's miraculous recovery. Hezekiah regally received them and showed them all the riches with which the Lord had blessed him. This flagrant demonstration of pride displeased the Lord, for in the thirty-first verse of the same chapter we read:

> Howbeit in the business of the ambassadors of the princes of Babylon, who sent unto him to inquire of the wonder that was done in the land, God left him, to try him, that he might know all that was in his heart.

Noting the use of the word "land" here, some heliocentric apologists have concluded that the sun only appeared to go back ten degrees just at the sundial site in Jerusalem or, on the basis of this verse, in the entire land of Israel. This makes the sign an optical illusion visible only from Jerusalem or Judea. Given just the two accounts seen thus far, such conclusion may be deemed feasible.

The third account of Hezekiah's sign is found in Isaiah 38:7-8 where we find some additional details:

> [7] And this shall be a sign unto thee from the LORD, that the LORD will do this thing that he hath spoken;
> [8] Behold, I will bring again the shadow of the degrees, which is gone down in the sun dial of Ahaz, ten degrees backward. So the sun returned ten degrees, by which degrees it was gone down.

The eighth verse forces a radical modification of the above conclusions, for it states that it was the sun, not just the shadow, that returned to retrace its path. This eliminates the conjecture that only the shadow on the dial was affected. So we are left with two alternatives: first, that the sun actually went back ten degrees as the Bible says; or second, in light of the reference to the "land" in 2 Chronicles, that the sun appeared to go back only in the land of Judah. But this second alternative discounts the fact that Isaiah 38:8 states quite explicitly that the "sun returned ten degrees." If it was only an optical phenomenon and not a real returning, should it not have been reported as such?

So what of the reference to "land" in 2 Chronicles 32:31? Does this not appear to contradict the sun's *actual* regression implicit in Isaiah 38:8? Note, however, that the 2 Chronicles passage speaks of the "wonder" instead of the "sign." It was the *wonder* that was done in the land. The wonder, as a whole, includes God's speaking to Hezekiah and his miraculous recovery, as well as the solar sign. Since Hezekiah was king of the land at the time, it would certainly be correct to refer to the wonder as being "done in the land" without limiting the scope of the effect of the sign to the land of Judah.

The straightforward reading of the three accounts of Hezekiah's sign indicates that the sign was global in extent and that the sun went back ten degrees in the sky, thus lengthening that day by forty minutes for the entire world. It also indicates that the sun did the moving, not the earth.

Degrees or Steps?

In their efforts to try and make these verses more "in accord with modern science," the authors of the modern Bible versions have ofttimes compounded the so-called contradictions. One ploy has been to cast doubt on the Hebrew Masoretic text. The translating committee of the *Revised Standard Version*, for example, ignores the Hebrew; and on the basis of one Syriac manuscript, replaces "by which it [the shadow] had gone down on the dial of Ahaz" with "by which the *sun* had declined on the dial of Ahaz." (Emphasis added.) By changing the subject from shadow to sun they present the ludicrous image of the sun descending the sundial as if it were walking down a series of steps. This linguistic error is repeated in Isaiah 38:8 after adding a footnote to the effect that the Hebrew is "obscure." Of course it is obscure if one is unwilling to admit to the biblical teaching of geocentricity.

The use of the word "degrees" has also been challenged. In his book, *The Astronomy of the Bible*, Maunder[1] constructed an elaborate scenario based on the use of "steps" instead of "degrees." Maunder speculated that the "steps" were part of the temple and that the Bible does not really refer to a sundial at all. He proposed that an accidental arrangement of temple pillars cast a shadow on a staircase built by Ahaz as a private entryway from his palace to the temple. In the course of the day, the shadows of the pillars would appear to "ascend" the staircase. In Maunder's opinion, the "sign" was a routine, daily occurrence and involved absolutely no change at all in the motion of the sun.

There are several problems with Maunder's speculation. Firstly, Ahaz so hated the Lord that he had the temple boarded up. It is most unlikely that he would build a special staircase linking the palace to the temple. Secondly, there is good reason to doubt that "steps" is the correct translation of the Hebrew word *mahalah*, and that "degrees" is correct.

In English, the word "degree" means $1/360^{th}$ part of a circle. Superficially, this would seem unique to modern times, for one might reasonably expect that today's system of measuring angles is different from that of the ancient Hebrews. One wonders just what fraction of a circle is represented by the Hebrew word *mahalah* (especially since it also appears in the prefaces to many of the Psalms). Bible critics insist that no one can know the correct meaning of *mahalah*, but it turns out that the Babylonians measured angles with a unit of measure whose name is almost identical to the Hebrew word under consideration. Interestingly, that Babylonian unit amounts to $1/360^{th}$ of a circle. This is exactly the definition of our modern degree. Thus the Authorized Translation is correct and modern versions miss the mark by changing "degrees" to "steps." Ten degrees means ten degrees after all; and, given that information, we know that the sun turning back ten degrees would lengthen that particular day by forty minutes.

Attempts at Naturalistic Explanations

Attempts to explain away Hezekiah's sign have produced some very unusual proposals. Some have suggested that there was an earthquake at Jerusalem which tilted the ground just enough to tip the sundial by ten degrees so that the shadow appeared to "go back" ten degrees. But then why was there no mention of the earthquake? It would certainly have been noted by Isaiah or by Hezekiah; and would the earthquake itself not have been enough of a sign? Others have suggested that the sundial was improperly mounted; and that as a result, the shadow only appeared to retrace its steps at certain times of the day. But if such were a daily occurrence then it would be no sign at all. Furthermore, no one has ever demonstrated just how a sundial might be mounted so that a shadow would retrace itself during the course of the day: such a "mismounting" is physically impossible. Certainly no regular sundial could accomplish such a feat; although Christopher Schissler of Augsburg, Germany, did in 1578 construct a bowl-shaped sundial which, upon water being poured into its bowl, will make the shadow of a wire go back as much as twenty degrees. It was not built as an explanation of the miracle but as a demonstration device.[2]

Another proposal is that there was a partial eclipse of the sun that day at Jerusalem. An eclipse of the sun happens when the moon passes between the sun and the earth, and a partial eclipse occurs in those places where the sun is not totally obscured. As a result, the shadow was "off-center" for the duration of the eclipse. Such a proposal may sound good on the surface but there are a couple of serious problems with it. First, if such an effect does happen during an eclipse, then it would at most amount to half of a degree, certainly not to ten degrees. Secondly, the closest eclipse to the usual date for the reign of Hezekiah, an eclipse visible from Jerusalem, was 11 January 689 B.C. That eclipse was over twenty years too late. Hezekiah was long dead by that time, let alone having another fifteen years to live. In short, there is no plausible alternative but to take the text literally.

One could, of course, discount the whole incident of the sign as a fabrication or as an elaboration of a quite natural event. Perhaps it was only local to the land of Judah. (Israel ceased to exist during the reign of Hezekiah, just prior to the sign.) But are there any other accounts of a similar event elsewhere in the world's folklore? We answer that question in the affirmative.

Hezekiah's Sign in India

The Hindus have a very long epic poem called the *Mahabharata*. The more widely known *Bhagavad Gita* is itself just a part of that epic poem. In section 146 of the *Mahabharata* there is an account of a war which the Hindus date as having happened about 3102 B.C. The story goes that the war was won by the forces of good because of a ruse by the sun god. It had been foretold that the evil forces would win if the battle did not end by nightfall. The battle proceeded until the sun set in its normal matter and the evil forces began their celebration. Unbeknownst to them, however, the forces of good had made a pact with the sun and as per agreement, the sun retraced its path, rose in the west, and stayed above the horizon for the greater part of an hour. This is precisely what would be expected if the effect were worldwide and occurred mid-afternoon Jerusalem time (about 3 p.m.). But what of the date? 3102 B.C. is a far cry from Hezekiah's reign which was roughly 700 B.C.

Actually, even Hindu scholars themselves discredit the 3102 B.C. date for the war mentioned in the *Mahabharata*. The majority of modern scholars date the war as happening sometime between 1500 B.C. and 800 B.C. Even at that, a date of 700 B.C. is not at all unlikely; nor is it inconsistent with available evidence. The poem seems to have been written about the sixth century B.C., about the time of Daniel. Even the history of the epic poem is fraught with exaggerated claims, and this is entirely consistent with the degree of unreliability of Indo-Persian historical reporting. For example, one hundred years after being conquered by the Greeks, the Persian historians had no recollection of ever having been conquered by anyone.

And so the *Mahabharata* account appears to describe the same event as Hezekiah's sign but in a different geographical location with an appropriately different time of day indicated.

Hezekiah's Sign in China

Not only do we have the Hindu account of Hezekiah's sign, but also we have a parallel account from China. According to Alfred Forke,[3] Huai-nan-tse tells us that in the fifth century B.C.:

> When the Duke of Lu-yang was at war against Han, during the battle the sun went down. The Duke, swinging his spear, beckoned to the sun, whereupon the sun, for his sake, came back and passed through three solar mansions.

This would have happened in western China. Further east, in the capitol, it would have been dark throughout the duration of the sign. Hezekiah's sign may account for another ancient Chinese report which states that at the time of Kingcungus, the planet Mars went back three degrees.[4] There is a problem with the "three degrees" for the regression of Mars. Since the Chinese degree is

$1/365.25^{th}$ of a circle, the three degrees are not nearly enough to match the ten degrees of scripture; but the measure would have been an estimate since there would have been no background stars relative to which to measure the angle. Furthermore, there may have been a delay of a half hour before a measurement relative to the ground could be made, assuming that the Chinese had both clocks and tables of planetary positions, which seems unlikely. There is yet another account, also mentioned in Forke, which tells that the king of Ch'in promised Prince Tan his freedom if the sun would go back, which it did.

Hezekiah's Sign in North America

If it is the case among the Chinese and Indians that the sun should set and come back up, what about tales of the sun rising and going back down. For these we must search the Americas. Robert H. Lowie reports such a tale: the story of Cottontail.[5] In the story, Cottontail devised a plan to kill all humanity and the sun. Digging a hole, he waited for the sun to rise. But the sun saw him and quickly dove back under. After a while the sun rose again; and after several failed attempts at killing the sun, Cottontail succeeded in knocking a piece of the sun off with a club. The world was set ablaze and the fire chased Cottontail who eventually found a fireproof weed in which to hide. After leaving the weed, the heat of the ground burned off three of his legs. Hopping on the fourth he built a shelter for the night. During the night it snowed, and the next day the sun changed Cottontail from a man into a rabbit.

The inconsistencies in the story are obvious: men don't have four legs, for example. But embroidery aside, here we do have an account of a sunrise followed by a solar retreat followed by another sunrise a while later: precisely as required by Hezekiah's sign.

The Menominee Indians of Michigan have a tale of the sun rising and then reverting to darkness. In their myth, two brothers were out hunting. One became tired and stopped to rest, but he did not get much rest because the sun kept teasing him. In revenge he obtained a hair from his sister and stretched it across the sun's path. Upon arising that morning, the sun was snared and started to choke. As a result, the sky became dark. A helpful mouse chewed through the hair and rescued the sun, thus restoring light to the earth.[6]

Yet another account reminiscent of Hezekiah's sign is told among the Indians of Northern California. According to their legend, the sun accidentally fell from the sky just about sunrise. A quick mole caught it before it touched the earth. After some time, help arrived, and they were able to restore the sun to the sky.[7]

Although the actual sunrise, retreat, and re-rising of the sun probably occurred far to the east, it also happened some 2,600 years before these stories were recorded. This is ample time for the tale to have spread. It is important to realize that, with only one exception, there are no sunset, retreat and re-setting tales in North America. The one exception is in California and may reflect a Chinese origin.

Hezekiah's Sign in the Central and South Americas

Turning our attention further south, a hesitation to rise on the part of the sun is recounted in Aztec folklore but appears as part of an account of a very long night. The two events may have been combined into one story later in Aztec history.[8] In the *Popol Vuh* there is an account of the horizon reddening and a subsequent darkening:

> But as it was about to dawn and the horizon reddened:
> "Make it dark again, old one!" the buzzard was told.
> "Very well," said the old one, and instantly the old one darkened the sky.[9]

In South America, Zechariah Sitchin[10] reports, Andean legends tell of a "brightening darkness." Although Sitchin takes it as a reference to Joshua's long day, the term "brightening darkness" seems more reasonable for a brightening with a subsequent return to darkness than it is for a lingering dawn. If so, then this could be a reference to Hezekiah's sign.

It is recorded[11] that in the Peruvian Andes there stand two ruined towers on opposite hills of a pass. Clamped to the walls there are iron hooks which, tradition has it, held a net designed to catch the rising sun. The local Indians report that the sun was caught once and held with a chain that allowed it only a little bit of up and down motion.[12] How it was released, for how long it was held, or how many times it bobbed up and down is not recorded.

The Peruvian tale seems to have traveled to Polynesia, for the Polynesians tell how their chief god, Maui, traveled far to the east to trap the sun in a net between two walls he had built for that purpose. It has long been suspected that the islands of the Pacific were settled from the east, from South America; the migration of the arrested, struggling sunrise throughout Polynesia to as far north as Hawaii (where Maui used a vine to trap the sun for his mother) lends credence to that supposition. As we shall see in the accounts of Joshua's long day, there is at least one account of the sun being snared at sunset. That tale has not migrated eastward, so that the predominant cultural influence seems to have come from the east.

We see here, as in the North American accounts, that the tales may have moved around geographically and have been embroidered quite a bit; but the basic theme is the same: the sun rose, went back, and then rose again. In some of the accounts it did not retreat far enough to the east to set, but it was very near the horizon. The conclusion is that the terminator (the line separating day from night) ran somewhere through the eastern United States and western South America.

Other Accounts

It is unlikely that many peoples would have noted a lengthened night since only the Egyptians had clocks, and a clock would be necessary to notice a forty-minute lengthening of the night. Few people in the Pacific Ocean basin, for example, would have been awake to see the stars turn back ten degrees.

One may question whether the stars participated in the retro-grade motion. If there are remnants of truth scattered throughout folk tales, we may conclude that they did. According to one Greek legend, Zeus settled an argument between two brothers as to which would become king of Mycenæ by reversing the course of the sun, Helios:

> Helios, already in mid-career, wrested his chariot about and turned his horses' heads towards the dawn. The seven Pleiades, and all the other stars, retraced their courses in sympathy; and that evening, for the first and last time, the sun set in the east.

Although the time of day at the start of the myth is correct for Hezekiah's sign (about 12:30 in the afternoon in Greece), adding at least seven hours to the day is inconsistent with the sun going back only ten degrees. Perhaps the Greek's time estimate was taken from (or else it inspired) the tract Sanhedrin 96a. According to the tract, God allowed only two hours of daylight the day of Ahaz's death so that there would not be any time for mourning or proper burial of the old king. The tract continues that the ten lost hours were restored by Hezekiah's sign. Despite all of this, the Bible clearly states "ten degrees," not ten hours; and it only takes forty minutes for the sun to move ten degrees.

The Time of the Sign

Given all of the above accounts at their respective values, it is possible to plot them on a globe to determine what time of day it was at Jerusalem when the sign happened. Doing so makes several things clear. The Chinese accounts seem the most reliable with the Indian account either originating from the easternmost borders of India or else being imported from Burma or China. It is not un-common for Indian folklore to be borrowed from the Chinese, so the latter assumption is reasonable. The terminator is in the proper position at about 1:30 p.m., Jerusalem time, give or take a half hour. Furthermore, it must have been in either late March to early April or else early to mid-September. The early spring is the most consistent with the snow mentioned in the Shoshone tale, for what that is worth.

Conclusion

Given these separate racial accounts, all of which are rather consistent with the day-and-night geography, there is no way to avoid the conclusion that there was a day in history when the day was lengthened by about forty minutes. One may argue as to whether the earth temporarily reversed in its daily rotation or that the sun and cosmos re-traced their daily paths by forty minutes, but unless one does not fear to call God a clumsy writer, the inescapable conclusion is that the uni-verse, sun in-cluded, backed up ten degrees and then re-sumed its regu-lar motions about the earth.

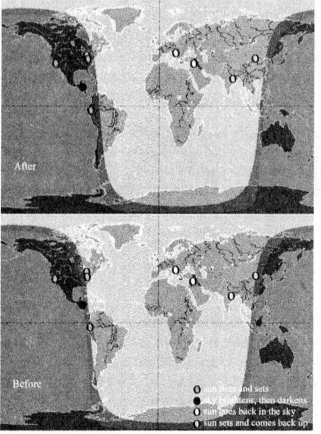

Figure 1: *Hezekiah's Sign before and after.*

O fools, and slow of heart to believe all
that the prophets have spoken ...

— Luke 24:25

5

JOSHUA'S LONG DAY

After leaving Egypt and wandering in the Sinai wilderness for
forty years, Israel entered the land of Canaan late March to
mid-April, 1448 B.C.[1] The Israelite leader, Joshua, had a clear-cut
task set before him: to completely eradicate all the previous inhabitants of the land. The story is quite familiar to every Sunday school
student: how the Israelites marched around Jericho until the city
fell, the subsequent defeat at Ai followed by the judgment of
Achan, the fall of Ai, and the ruse of the Gibeonites who tricked
the Israelites into an unholy alliance. When the surrounding nations heard of that alliance, they attacked the Gibeonites who then
sent to Joshua for help. The account of the battle that followed oc-
cupies about half of the tenth chapter of the book of Joshua where
verses twelve through fourteen tell of the peculiar event which is
commonly called *Joshua's long day*:

> [12] Then spake Joshua to the LORD in the day when the
> LORD delivered up the Amorites before the children of Is-
> rael and he said in the sight of Israel, Sun, stand thou still
> upon Gibeon; and thou, Moon, in the valley of Ajalon.
> [13] And the sun stood still, and the moon stayed, until the
> people had avenged themselves upon their enemies. Is not
> this written in the book of Jasher? So the sun stood still in
> the midst of heaven, and hasted not to go down about a
> whole day.
> [14] And there was no day like that before it or after it, that
> the LORD hearkened unto the voice of a man: for the
> LORD fought for Israel.

Reactions of the Commentators

The geocentric implication of this passage is obvious. Instead of the sun's motion through the sky being due to the rotation of the earth, here it states that the sun and moon daily move around the earth. The sun is commanded not to move or rise; it is not the earth which receives the commandment to stop turning. Over the last 400 years, this has been the source of much consternation among the commentators and Bible critics — both higher and lower critics. Their reactions fall into two main categories: those who wish to make the event to be a fiction and those who try to accommodate the account to modern science's insistence that the earth rotates daily on its axis. In either case, it is science that is held to be correct, and it is the Bible which is held to be in error and which must be conformed to modern belief.

Those who try to accommodate Joshua's long day to science fall into two groups. The first group includes those critics who try to blame the geocentric "flaw" in Joshua 10 on faulty transmission of the text or, at least, to faulty translation or a misunderstanding of what God meant to say. The second group consists of those who try to make of the event an illusion or else a quite natural occurrence. Generally, both groups will admit of a miracle, but not all will admit to a miracle in the sky; and all make the miracle something less than the Bible claims it to be.

The Fiction Faction

Bible critics who claim that Joshua's long day is a fiction or allegory have contributed a great deal to our understanding of the event. Their main thrust is to disprove the account by showing either that there are no independent accounts and that Joshua 10 stands alone, or else to show that all accounts derive from one sun-stopping myth. The latter, for example, would be demonstrated if all accounts the world over stopped the sun in daytime. As a result of their efforts, we have a wide selection of tales to evaluate; and they do prove useful in understanding Joshua's long day as a worldwide event. We shall look at those geographically unrelated accounts later in this chapter.

One of the fundamental assumptions of the fiction faction is that the Bible is the product of the human mind. This assumption is really what lies behind the agenda to collect the so-called "sun-catcher myths." If Joshua's long day is pure fiction, then the whole Bible may be relegated to the trashcan as nothing more than a pack of lies and fables. After all, if Joshua 10:12-14 cannot be trusted, what can be trusted in the Bible? The Bible claims itself inerrant. It either is or it is not. The fiction faction has decided that Joshua's long day, if not the whole Bible, is bunk. What's interesting is that most of those who have decided that are not yet ready to banish the Bible to the landfills of history.

Adjusting the Language

Not all Bible critics are ready to throw out the Bible on the basis of the apparent conflict between the geocentric implications of Joshua's long day and modern science's heliocentric leanings. Many bend over backward to accommodate the Bible to science on this and other points. As far as Joshua's long day is concerned, some have suggested that the effect was psychological, that the day only *seemed* supernaturally long. Deane made that proposal with these words:

> ...the Israelites may well have regarded the events of that one day as equivalent to the work of two, and thus in course of time it came to be believed in current tradition that the day was prolonged to twice its usual length, though Scripture itself nowhere supported the statement.[2]

There is one basic problem which must be dealt with by all who would wish to maintain that the actual time elapsed involved fifteen hours or less of daylight. Given the geography as related in Joshua 10, the Israelite army as a whole marched well over thirty miles. Any army would be hard pressed to march thirty miles in

one day, let alone to fight as well. The larger the army; the slower
it moves. Yet if Deane is correct, not only did the army march
thirty miles, but it also fought a full-fledged battle as well, and all in
twelve hours of daylight, (it being late March or April when these
events took place). Deane, of course, assumes that men and not
God authored the Bible. If that is the case, then the Bible can be
safely ignored since God cannot be held accountable for the blun-
ders of humanity.

It is very common to find commentators claiming that the Hebrew is mistranslated or misunderstood whenever the Bible disagrees with their notion of what it should say. When applied to
Joshua's long day, for example, one proposal is that the words
"stand still" are better understood as "be silent" or "be still." Doing so caused the nineteenth century astronomer Maunder to claim
that Joshua meant nothing more than that there be an end to the
blazing noonday heat. According to Maunder, the miracle was the
sudden appearance of storm clouds from the Mediterranean Sea.[3]
To this Bernard Ramm concurs.[4]

Collett argues the same, claiming that the Hebrew should be
translated "be inactive" or "be silent." He then makes this as-
toundingly unscientific statement:

> We have already seen that light is vocal, and it is generally
> held among scientific men that it is the action of the sun
> upon the earth that causes the latter to revolve [sic] upon its
> axis.[5]

In Collett's opinion, light not only speaks, but sunlight shining
on the earth is what causes the earth's rotation. So, according to
Collett, when the sun stopped shining at Joshua's request, the earth
stopped turning because there was no longer any sunlight to keep it
turning. Both opinions are scientifically preposterous, especially
the latter.

Boling[6] presents a look at the schizophrenia inherent in the "be
silent" proposal. Although he translates Joshua 10:13 as "Sun was
stilled and Moon stood fixed"; and so admits the interpretation "be
still": and although he allows that the Hebrew may mean "to be

clouded over," he believes that Joshua's long day was an eclipse. Significantly, despite the above admission that the Hebrew might mean to "be still," he finally contradicts his own translation by concluding that the Hebrew can only mean "stay put," "hold a position," or "strike a pose."[7]

But the introduction of clouds to cover the sun could not in the least account for the report of the thirteenth verse that the "sun stood still" and the "moon stayed." The only way that the Hebrew word *dawmam* could be translated as "silent" would be if the sun were making so much noise that it was either disrupting the battle or Joshua's concentration. And, lest anyone doubt God's ability to tell us plainly when the sun is covered with clouds, we present Ezekiel 32:7 for his consideration:

> And when I shall put thee out, I will cover the heaven, and make the stars thereof dark; I will cover the sun with a cloud, and the moon shall not give her light.

Be that as it may, having Joshua say "stand still" to the sun does not change the content of the thirteenth verse where the sun is said to stand still. Generally, the commentators can get Joshua off the "scientific" hook, but they have no luck at all getting God off the hook in the thirteenth verse; it still reads that the sun "hasted not to go down about a whole day."

Take the Ferar Fenton version from the early twentieth century as an example. Fenton rendered the twelfth and thirteenth verses of Joshua 10 as:

> [12] Joshua also called to the Ever-living on that day: "Jehovah! Give the Amorites to the face of the children of Israel!" and he added, "Sun! In the eyes of Israel be still at Gibeon, and Moon! in the valley of Ailan!"
> [13] And the sun and moon stood still, till the nation had mastered its foes! Is not this recorded in the true Record? — that the sun stood still in mid sky, and hastened not to set for about a full day?

Note how Fenton saved Joshua from making the "error" of thinking that the sun goes around the earth by having the words "in the eyes of Israel" be part of the quote rather than the commentary. Fenton may have saved Joshua's pride, but God is still left "holding the bag" in the thirteenth verse, where the commentator's words have not been changed. Fenton wrote in his foreword that his version was the "first ever" in which the translator "used his brain"!

The Jewish Commentators

Oddly, only the Gentile commentators "know" enough Hebrew to notice that Joshua told the sun to be still: it seems to have escaped the Jewish commentators. Jewish scholars, both those who believed in the miracle and those who did not, make no such distinction in their writings; even among heliocentrists. One of the earliest Jewish commentators extant is Philo, who is notorious for bad paraphrasing and interpolating his own ideas into the Jewish text and history. His account:

> And when Jesus arose to rule over the people, it came to pass in the day wherein he fought against the enemies, that the evening drew near, while the battle was strong, and Jesus said to the sun and the moon: O ye ministers that were appointed between the Most Mighty and his sons, lo now, the battle goeth still, and do ye forsake your office? Stand still therefore today and give light unto his sons, and put darkness upon our enemies. And they did so.[8]

Note, no mention of "be silent."

Manasseh Ben Israel summarized the mainline Jewish opinions on Joshua's long day this way:[9]

> Rabbi Levi Ben Gershon [Spain, circa 1300], philosophizing in the extreme, holds that the sun did not stop..., it is the agency of the mind that performs miracles...so that the miracle consists in taking revenge in so short a period.

In Spain, in the last half of the twelfth century, Maimonides taught that Joshua's long day was "a most perfect day, that is like the longest summer day." In other word, Maimonides did not believe it was a miracle. On the other hand, most Rabbis did believe in a long day, though they differed in opinion on how long the day ultimately was. Rabbi Joshua Ben Levi of Jerusalem about A.D. 200 advocates 24 hours. Three hundred years earlier, about 100 B.C., Rabbi Eliezer, also of Jerusalem, argued for a day of 36 hours. Rabbi Samuel Bar Nachman who lived around A.D. 320 held to a 48-hour day. So Jewish opinion was as divided as Christian opinion about what constituted Joshua's long day.

The consensus of the early Jewish commentators is clear: none invoke the "be silent" approach. So they agree with Boling's conclusion, mentioned earlier, that "be silent" and its variant forms are not valid translations of the Hebrew. As a result, the validity of adjusting the language to accommodate Joshua's long day to science is thrown into question. There seems to be no basis left for doing so.

It's Only Natural

The second of the accommodation groups is those who advocate a naturalistic explanation for Joshua's long day. We have already seen one such explanation when we looked at the suggestion that the Bible's language be adjusted to mean that Joshua's long day was nothing more than a cloud cover to cool the heat of the day. Related to this idea, and also stemming from the "be silent" interpretation, is the opinion that Joshua's long day is an eclipse of the sun.

Was Joshua's Long Day an Eclipse?

An eclipse of the sun happens when the moon passes in front of the sun as seen from earth. If one is within about 100 miles from the center of the moon's shadow, one may see a *total eclipse* of the sun, at which point the sun's disk is obscured and one sees a halo around the sun (called the *corona*). An eclipse of the sun still inspires fear and awe among peoples of all nations. As a result, even though Babylonian astronomers were able to predict eclipses at the time of Joshua scholars still consider it reasonable to suppose that Israel's enemies were terrified out of their wits by the sudden appearance of an eclipse. So it is that some critics even claim that it was the eclipse, and not God, that caused Israel's enemies to flee.

Robert Dick Wilson (1856-1930) is regarded by many as the foremost linguistic scholar of the nineteenth and twentieth centuries. In 1930, he published an essay dealing with Joshua's long day.[10] Fully aware of the error of rendering the Hebrew as "be silent," Wilson took another common approach among Bible critics, which is to look to a similar language to get the meaning he wanted. In his case, he looked to the Babylonian.

Before we examine Wilson's work, let us give an example of how this approach can turn out. Many have commented on the similarities between English and Hebrew, on the many Hebrew words which are to be found in English. It has even been said that of all the modern languages, English is the closest to Hebrew. Now suppose I am translating some English text into French and I come upon the English sentence "She hit me!" Now we all know that girls are not supposed to hit people; only boys hit people. Suppose I then conclude that the author of the original English sentence cannot have meant what he wrote. Perhaps a copyist error has crept into the text. On the basis of the similarities between English and Hebrew, I may conclude that they are cognate. Now in Hebrew, the sound "he" means "she" in English, and the sound "she" is equivalent to the English "he." So, since English is cognate to Hebrew, the "correct" translation into French of "She hit me!" must be "He hit me!" Using cognate languages to change interpretations of "difficult" Bible passages is done all too commonly.

After replacing the Hebrew words with their Babylonian meanings, Wilson concluded that:

...the day of the battle had two comings-out of the sun, one at sunrise and the other at midday, when it came out from behind the moon; and that it had two goings-in, one when it went behind the moon and the other at sunset.[11]

On that basis, Wilson provides us with the following translation of Joshua 10:12-13:

[12] Be eclipsed, O Sun, in Gibeon, And thou moon in the valley of Ajalon!
[13] And the sun was eclipsed and the moon turned back, while the nation was avenged on its enemies. Is it not written upon the book of Jashar? And the sun stayed in the half of the heavens, And set not hastily as when a day is done.[12]

Now note that the geocentric "error" has been transferred to the book of Jasher. Wilson had thus spared himself the shame and embarrassment of being regarded as an ignorant Bible thumper, for he writes:

I confess to a feeling of relief, as far as I myself am concerned, that I shall no longer feel myself forced by strict exegesis to believe that the Scriptures teach that there actually occurred a miracle involving so tremendous a reversal of all the laws of gravitation. It can readily be understood how the Jewish interpreters of latter times, either through ignorance, or because of their overwhelming desire to magnify their own importance in the scheme of the universe, should have embraced the opportunity that the ambiguous terms of this purely scientific account afforded them to enhance the magnitude of the divine interference on their behalf.[13]

Wilson is not alone in his belief that Joshua's long day was an eclipse of the sun. Boling[14] promotes the eclipse of September 30, 1131 B.C. as the very eclipse. Unfortunately, that is more than 200 years too late, given the biblical chronology.[15] Faulstich is of a different opinion. He prefers the eclipse of April 19, 1421 B.C.[16]

Although an eclipse makes sense if Joshua wanted to frighten his enemies and to diminish the heat of the day, there are some problems with this approach. Insofar as the heat of the day is concerned, any relief granted the Israelites would also be granted Israel's enemies. More importantly, an eclipse is of a short duration, lasting at most eight minutes. Since the eclipse was already scheduled in God's timetable, how can Joshua 10:14 report that God had listened to the voice of a man? Faulstich answers this by saying that God had Joshua's request in mind when he created the sun and moon and when he set the moon into orbit around the earth. In any case, there is no miracle involved, only a natural event.

The strongest support the eclipse advocates claim is found in Joshua 10:12, where Joshua tells the sun to stand still *over* Gibeon and the moon *in* the valley of Ajalon. Since there is only a matter of a few miles separating the two sites, how can the verse be literally true unless both the sun and moon were directly overhead? In that case, the moon must have been covering the sun, the very situation known as an eclipse.

In response, it must be noted that Joshua is speaking as a man (verse 14) and thus not speaking an inspired revelation. Joshua could be using the language of appearance, an error which God cannot afford to commit. Note that the date is mid- to late-April. The sun at the time is overhead along a circle no further north than one touching the southern-most tip of the Red Sea. Even at its furthest point north (the first day of summer) the sun is overhead only in a circle running through southern Egypt. Gibeon is a good seven degrees further north. The sun is never overhead at Gibeon and never has been in all recorded biblical history. The second thing we note is that the moon is far larger than the valley of Ajalon. Taking Joshua's statement literally would have flattened the entire scene as the moon came down to rest in the valley. It is evident that Joshua could see the moon "in" the valley in order to tell it to stand still. If the moon were close enough to the sun for an eclipse, Joshua would not have seen the moon until the eclipse was actually under way. Why did he not then tell it, too, to stand still "over" the city of Gibeon? So it is that our conclusion is that Joshua was speaking phenomenologically when he told the sun to stand still *over* Gibeon and the moon *in* the valley of Ajalon, and that God did not put the words into his mouth in Joshua 10:12. (Also see verse 14.) By contrast, in the thirteenth verse God does not repeat Joshua's error of speaking phenomenologically.

The Refraction Rationalization

In Chapter 5 we saw that one of the rationalizations for Hezekiah's sign was that it was an optical illusion. The same has been proposed for Joshua's long day. Keil and Delitsch are among those who hold that both Hezekiah's sign and Joshua's long day were optical phenomena:

> an optical stoppage of the sun, or rather a continuance of visibility of the sun above the horizon.[17]

Basic behind this proposal is that the rotation of the earth did not stop but that God miraculously bent the light rays of the sun and moon so that, in Canaan at least, the sun and moon appeared to remain above the horizon. Yet the plain wording of the text is that the "sun stopped" and "the moon stayed"; it does not say that God "kept the light of the sun and moon" shining over the battlefield. Now God could have said that, but he did not.

The Gradual Slowdown

Until about the middle of this century, most critics of Joshua's long day had the earth suddenly stopping its rotation. Such a catastrophic change, unless it were supernaturally controlled, would have to occur very slowly or else the earth would be torn to pieces and the oceans would have left their basins and washed over the continents. Recognizing this problem in the mid-nineteenth century, Gaussen[18] dealt extensively on how God could slow down the earth's rotation for Joshua without causing those earthly catastrophes. In the Twentieth Century, the strongest proponent of the rotation slowdown was Immanuel Velikovsky who proposed that the earth was tidally slowed in its rotation by a close passage of the planet Venus and then sped up again to its original rotation speed when Venus left.[19]

Now there is no hint in Joshua 10 that there was a gradual slowing of the diurnal motion, but we can give an analogy which will enable an appreciation of the problem as it is commonly defined. Since the equatorial rotation speed of the earth is about 1,000 miles per hour, which is the same speed as a jet fighter, we can use the slowing of a jet plane for comparison. Suppose there is no turbulence buffeting the jet and suppose that there is a saucer of water in the plane. The problem is to stop the plane without sloshing the water out of the saucer. A little experimentation shows that one may decelerate the dish at about 0.5 miles per hour per second without spilling the water. If so, we conclude that it would take about 35 minutes to stop the earth's rotation without the oceans leaving their basins. Such may work for a saucer, but oceans are much deeper and have much more energy. Small shifts in the ocean bottom have been known to cause huge waves, for example. Still, 35 minutes, though optimistic, is not an unreasonable response time to Joshua's request. A further problem is that the atmosphere does not behave as well as the ocean in this regard. The air near the earth's surface would slow down first, but the air aloft would keep going, dragging the air below with it. The slowdown time needed to avoid 1,000 mile-per-hour winds scouring the earth's equator amounts to days, a most unreasonable time to respond to Joshua's request. Lest the reader conclude that the geocentric explanation has no such problem, we note that the geocentric case suffers the same problems. Insofar as the slowing-down of the earth's rotation is concerned, there is no way to escape the conclusion that Joshua's long day was a miracle.

The Tippie-Top

Increasingly, heliocentric apologists have tried to abstract the meaning of the sun's arrest to such a degree that the actual intent of the passage is virtually unrecognizable. Howard Rand suggested that perhaps the axis of rotation of the earth changed in such a way that for about one day the battle site became the rotational north pole.[20] Although not original with Rand, the idea has gained popularity lately because of the influence of Velikovsky.

In the tippie-top scenario, some event inside the earth or else the fly-by of some planetary body caused the earth's rotational poles to move in such a way that, for one day, Joshua's battle site was at the north pole. One obvious problem is that the moon would still be seen to go around the sun during the battle. But the text says that the moon, too, stood still.

Not so obviously, Professor James Hanson of the Cleveland State University in Cleveland, Ohio, has shown mathematically that Rand's is not a possible explanation. Furthermore, Hanson also has shown that the explanation of Joshua's long day as proposed by Velikovsky is physically impossible unless Venus were still orbiting the earth today in an orbit even closer to the earth than is the moon.[21] In fact, none of the naturalistic proposals put forth to account for Joshua's long day are physically possible. The simple choice remains: Joshua's long day is either a miracle, or it is pure fiction.

The Book of Jasher

There is one other tact which a handful of commentators have taken in order to allegorize or else account for Joshua's long day, and that is to assign parts of Joshua 10:12-14 to the book of Jasher mentioned in the thirteenth verse. It is their suggestion that there never was a miracle, that Joshua merely asked the sun to be "stilled," and centuries later some nameless "editor" incorporated the fictional account of the sun standing still from an uninspired book entitled the *Book of Jasher*. The word, *jasher,* means "upright" or "just." The term could just as well refer to the Bible itself as to any other book. Nevertheless, there is a book in existence today which some claim is the very *Book of Jasher* mentioned in Joshua. This seems extremely unlikely, however, since that *Book of Jasher* was apparently written sometime after the time of David as it contains several poems attributed to David. Most Christian commentators believe the book to be a forgery, written because the biblical reference afforded the occasion for its creation. The text of the *Book of Jasher* exalts the heroic deeds of the great men of Israel, but the men exalted therein were not necessarily righteous men, the title to the contrary. Then, as now, a nation's "great men" are seldom righteous and just. It appears, then, that the real *Book of Jasher* referred to in scripture is either the Bible itself, as the book of the upright and righteous, or else it refers to a long-lost book.

Joshua's Long Day around the World?

Having concluded that Joshua's long day is a miracle, we may ask whether or not it was restricted just to the area of Canaan or whether it was global in scope. Certainly a "missing day" would generate considerable consternation among the peoples of the world, provided it was a global event. Are there other accounts of a long day or even a long night? Indeed, we can find stories of a long night as well as a long day. We can even find tales where the sun hung near the horizon for a long time. All the accounts taken together allow us to ascertain the time of day when Joshua told the sun to stand still.

Some of the world's recitations of Joshua's long day are vague and unspecific while others are quite clear. Among the former are those which relate only that the people had knowledge of the concept that the sun, moon, and stars can reverse their motions. An example of one of these is the account referred to by Augustine in *The City of God* where he quotes the Æneid about a witch who:

> ...can reverse the wheeling of the planets, halt rivers in their flowing.[22]

Joshua's Long Day in Africa

Toward the end of the last century, Charles Adiel Lewis Totten, then a retired Professor of Military Science from Yale University, published a controversial study on Joshua's long day.[23] The book dealt extensively with Joshua's long day and Hezekiah's sign. In recent times attempts to discredit it center more on the person of Totten than they do on the mathematics and science involved. Totten was the editor of *Our Race,* a publication devoted to the promotion of what today is called "British Israelitism"; although Totten's stance is eminently more realistic and moderate than that taken by that faction today. Robert Olden[24] says Totten obtained most of his material from J. B. Dimbleby of South Hackney, England, who was the premier chronologist of the British Chronological Society. Lest Totten be accused of plagiarism, Dimbleby is cited numerous times in Totten's works. Totten has also been accused of worshipping the Great Pyramid of Giza, from which, it is claimed, he received his inspiration for his work on Joshua's long day. Actually, the latter sounds more like Dimbleby, for a reading of Totten's works on the Great Pyramid reveals none of the mysticism implied by the charge.

Anyhow, flawed though some of Totten's works might be, in his book, he relates two independent and geographically distinct accounts of Joshua's long day. One of Totten's sources is a report by the Greek historian Herodotus who wrote that when he visited Egypt, the priests there showed him an ancient manuscript which told the story of a day which lasted about twice as long as a normal day. Now the Egyptians had water clocks at that time so that they could accurately measure the duration of the day, not being dependent on the motion of the sun, moon, and stars as would other peoples around the world. Totten's second account is from the Chinese which we shall present later.

For the Egyptian account, we find that the French classical scholar, Fernand Crombette, translated some Egyptian hieroglyphics which tell of Joshua's long day.[25] The text starts out with an edict from the king to exempt from taxation those who had been victims of a flood some two weeks earlier. Evidently the flood had been caused by an unusually high tide. The cause, according to the Egyptian hieroglyphics, was:

> The sun, thrown into confusion, had remained low on the horizon, and by not rising had spread terror amongst the great doctors. Two days had been rolled into one. The morning was lengthened to one-and-a-half times the normal period of effective daylight. A certain time after this divine phenomenon, the master had an image built to keep further misfortune from the country.
>
> Hephaistos . . . grant protection to your worshipers. Prevent the words of these foreign travelers from having any effect. They are impostors. Let these enemies of the sacrifices to the images be destroyed in the temples of the great gods by the people of all classes. Make life harder for these cursed worshipers of the Eternal. Punish them. Increase the hardships of these shepherds. Reduce the size of their herds. Burn their dwellings.
>
> Rameses, our celestial ancestral chief; you who forced these wretched people to work, who ill-treated them, who gave them no help when they were in need: cast them into the sea. They made the moon stop in a small angle at the edge of the horizon. In a small angle on the edge of the horizon, the sun itself, which had just risen at the spot where the moon was going, instead of crossing the sky stayed where it was. Whilst the moon, following a narrow path, reduced its speed and climbed slowly, the sun stopped moving and its intensity of light was reduced to the brightness at daybreak. The waves formed a wall of water against the boats that were in the harbor and those that had left it. Those fishermen that had ventured onto the deck to watch the waves were washed into the sea.
>
> The tide, which had risen high, overflowed into the plains where the herds were grazing. The cattle drowned represented half the herds of Lower Egypt. The remains of abandoned boats broken against the sides of the canals were

piled up in places. Their anchors, which should have protected them, had been ground into them. Quite out of control, the sea had penetrated deep into the country. The expanding waters reached the fortified walls constructed by Rameses, the celestial ancestral chief. The sea swept around both sides of the region behind, sterilizing the gardens as it went and causing openings in the dikes. A great country had been turned into a wilderness and brought into poverty. All the crops that had been planted had been destroyed and heaps of cereal shoots lay scattered on the ground.

The Crombette account is significant for a number of reasons. For one, it tells that the moon "climbed slowly," which would be correct if the moon kept its orbital speed but stopped its daily motion. This is allowed by Joshua 10:13's weaker statement on the moon: "and the moon stayed," instead of the stronger "stopped," for "stay" may mean "to linger or wait to witness an event." Likewise, Crombette's interpretation that the moon was going to the spot where the sun had risen is thus explained by having the moon continue its orbital motion and its being located west of the sun, perhaps near last quarter.

Whether or not the tides mentioned in translation were really tides or a storm swell cannot be said. It is possible that the tidal bulge kept moving, but it is unlikely that the narrows of the Nile delta and the narrowness of the canals mentioned caused a bore wave, for then such should always have been the case under normal tidal conditions. It is possible, though unlikely, that the breakup for the tidal bulge may have caused waves which interfered with each other and that Egypt's dikes might have broken at one or two points by constructive interference, thus the resulting flooding. But it seems more likely that the events mentioned in Egypt were the result of a severe storm swell in the Mediterranean caused by the very storm that formed the hailstones mentioned in Joshua 10:11:

And it came to pass, as they fled from before Israel, and were in the going down to Bethhoron, that the LORD cast down great stones from heaven upon them unto Azekah, and they died: they were more which died with hailstones than they whom the children of Israel slew with the sword.

Although most commentators insist that Joshua's long day started at noon or later, the sun is here mentioned low on the horizon. The Bible itself does not mention the time when Joshua spake. For comparison with the Egyptian account, and complementing it, there is a West African story of a long night.[26] In that account, the night lasted way too long because the owl overslept and did not awaken the sun.

The Chinese Account of Joshua's Long Day

The second secular source about Joshua's long day which was mentioned by Totten is based on what seems to be a recently lost ancient Chinese manuscript. In 1810, John Gill presented this account:

In the Chinese history[27] it is reported, that in the time of their seventh emperor, Yao, the sun did not set for ten days, and that men were afraid the world would be burnt, and there were great fires at that time; and though the time of the sun's standing still were enlarged beyond the bounds of truth, yet it seems to refer to this fact, and was manifestly about the same time; for this miracle was wrought in the year of the world 2554, which fell in the 75th, or, as some say, the 67th year of that emperor's reign, who reigned 90 years.[28]

Now the year of the world 2554 is identical to Bouw's independently derived biblical chronology for the date of Joshua's long day.[29] Incidentally, note that a 90-year reign (not Yao's age) is thoroughly consistent with the 110 to 120 year ages achieved by Moses, Aaron, and Joshua who would have been contemporaries of

Yao. The length of time mentioned by the Chinese, ten days, may be too long simply because the Chinese did not have clocks which ran independently of the sun's motion so that the estimate would be purely subjective. Probably, the duration was exaggerated both by the trauma of the event and in the transmission of the story through time.

Despite the solid-sounding account by Gill, manuscripts which have survived to the twentieth century do not include the long day. The first mention of the long day associated with emperor Yao was by Hübner in 1733.[30] Although Hübner was quoted during that century, no manuscript exists today. Those manuscripts which have survived to this day differ from Hübner's in at least two ways: first, there is no mention of the ten-day day, and second, the reign of Yao is reported to be 100 years, not 90.

Although there is no mention of the ten-day long day in current Chinese accounts, there is one in the "Brahman Yast," one of the books of the *Avesta*. That reference is not, however, to a past event. Instead, it is a prophecy. The *Avesta* says that 1600 years from the date of the Persian culture (corresponding to about A.D. 1200), Hushedar will be born and, at age 30, he will command the sun to stand still for 10 days and nights. Obviously, the prophecy never came to pass; still it is strongly reminiscent of the Chinese account and may either have confused Hübner or else may reflect the actual Chinese account used by Hübner.

Joshua's Long Day in North America

Tales relating to Joshua's long day abound in North America. Almost all of the tales in North America tell of a long night. The only exceptions are those related in the chapter on Hezekiah's sign. Olcott[31] has collected five of particular interest. 1) The Ojibways tell of a long night without any light.[32] 2) The Wyandot Indians told missionary Paul Le Jeune of a long night.[33] 3) The Dogrib Indians of the Northwest tell of a day when the sun was caught at noon and it instantly became dark.[34] 4) The Omahas say that once the sun was caught in a trap by a rabbit that checked its traps at the

break of dawn, presumably before sunrise.[35] (This may be Hezekiah's sign, too.)   Finally, 5) the Bungee Indians from the Lake
Winnipeg area of Canada also tell of a long night.[36]

The preponderance of long night tales in the Americas would
rule out the theory that Joshua's long day was a miracle which was
local to Canaan. It also rules out the speculation that the story migrated around the world, for then it would everywhere be a long
day (or a long night), but not a mixture of long days and long
nights.

The Long Night in the Central and South Americas

Turning to the south, we find that Central and South America
similarly experienced a long night. In the *Annals of Chauhtitlan,*
the Mexican Indians tell of a long night. The Aztecs wrote of an extended period of time when the sun did not rise. According to their
legend, there had been no sun for many years.

> ... So a conclave of the gods was called in Teotihuacan, and
> there it was decided that one of them should offer himself as a
> sacrifice that once again the world might have a sun ... The sacri-
> ficed gods had disappeared in the brazier's flames, but as there
> was no sign of the sun, the remaining wonder when it would first
> appear. At long last, the sun burst forth ... But the sun, despite
> his brilliant light, did not move; he hung on the edge of the sky,
> apparently unwilling to begin his appointed task.[37]

Likewise, in their national book the *Popol Vuh,* (which translates
into "Book of the Princes,") the Quiche- Mayans of Guatemala wrote
about the people's reaction to a long night with these words:

> They did not sleep; they remained standing and great was the
> anxiety of their hearts and their stomachs for the coming of the
> dawn and the day ... "Oh, ... if we only could see the rising of
> the sun! What shall we do now?" ... They talked, but they
> could not calm their hearts which were anxious for the
> coming of the dawn.[38]

Now in recent years it is fashionable to assail the above translations on the grounds that they are biased towards the Judeo-Christian history of the world. For example, the Aztec god who sacrificed himself was to have the honor of becoming the sun. His condition for rising was that the gods kill themselves, which they ultimately were forced to do.[39] It would seem that this is a creation myth rather than an account of Joshua's long day, but the nature of Central American folk tales is very complex. For example, according to the myth there had been a sun before, and it had not risen for so long that people feared it dead. So how is it a creation account?

A similar situation exists with the *Popol Vuh*. According to some, that entire work is nothing more than one long creation myth. But the creation of man comes very late in the *Popol Vuh,* long after people have existed and had many adventures. The text quoted above from Goetz and Morley lies embedded in a lengthy section which starts with the longing and waiting for the sun, digresses into the origin of fire, and makes mention of the parting of the sea for the newly-arrived forefathers before resuming the story of the long wait for the dawn. If this is a creation account which occurred before the creation of man and which speaks of the creation of the sun, why are there many priests and tribes in existence? Why the reference to the forefathers who existed then if man had yet to be created? Such situations are typical in the literature of that region and time, and it may easily be understood in the light of the purpose of these tales: they exist to tie together salient pieces of history. So it is, too, with the Aztec tale. There was a long night, but the story has been expanded almost beyond recognition. Similarly with the *Popol Vuh* there is evidence of changes in the tale even over the last few centuries.

As for the charge that early translators were biased, are the anti-Christian translators not equally biased for their view? The fact remains, there is a reference here to a long night, exactly as would be expected if the various accounts around the world of Joshua's long day were true.

Besides the accounts of a long night in North and Central America, there is also at least one story of a long night in Peru.

According to Montesinos, the collector of the tale, the sun was hidden for nearly 20 hours in the third year of the reign of Titu Yupanqui Pachacuti II because of sin in the land.[40] Titu Yupanqui Pachacuti II ruled about 1400 B.C.

The Long Sunset

Stories of a long day and stories of a long night: are there any stories of a long sunrise or a long sunset? There may be some uncollected stories of a long sunrise in Africa, but none have surfaced. There is, however, a story of a long sunset in the Fiji Islands. J. G. Frazer tells of a tradition on the island of Lakomba in the eastern Fiji Islands where there is a hillside with a patch of weeds on it. The story goes that natives will tie the weeds together in order to keep the sun from going down. It is said that the sun did, indeed, stop from setting at one time.[41]

Although there are several other traditions of stopping the sun, most are remotely, if at all, connected to Joshua's long day. In Australia, for example, if a native wanted to stop the sun he would place a piece of sod in the fork of a tree. Similar traditions exist in Africa and in Central America. A tradition of that nature in Japan meant nothing more than the belief that a man's friends would await dinner for him if he was going to arrive home late. Still, underlying all but the last of these traditions is the idea that the sun can, and by implication, did stop at least once upon a time.

The Extra-Long Night

A small handful of long day and long night tales do not seem to fit. The Hawaiian tale of Maui's capture of the sun is one, for it implies an arrest of the sun at sunrise. It is similar to the myths from other Polynesian Islands peoples, and those similarities serve to tie it to Peru's Hezekiah's sign accounts, not Joshua's long day.

Three peoples have a tale of a night which lasted several months: the Japanese, an ancient tribe in Lithuania, and the Cherokee Indians of North America. The Cherokee and Japanese tales are virtually identical and seem to stem from the same source. Both have the sun hiding in a cave for a long time and being tricked out of the cave.[42]

The account from Lithuania was collected by Jerome of Prague when he visited the "heathen" of the area in the early 15th century. There he discovered a tribe which had migrated from the east and which also told tales of a night lasting several months.

There are two possible reasons for these accounts. All could be related to the Japanese account and could reflect either a volcanic eruption which darkened the sky over Japan and Siberia for months on end or else, it could be a tale of the long Arctic night, almost six months long at the pole. A two-month night is experienced about the latitude of Point Barrow, Alaska. Perhaps the accounts relate to these natural events. In any case, they stand in stark contrast with the other long day and long night tales from around the world.

Joshua's Long Day and the Computers

In the late 1970s and early 1980s two stories appeared in print about a computer finding a missing day. The first is told by Harold Hill in his book, *How to Live Like a King's Kid*.[43] In Hill's own words:

> When NASA's Goddard Space Flight Center here at Greenbelt, Md. first went on the air, a horrendous technical boo-boo surfaced, causing a complete shutdown [of the computer] after less than an hour's operation.
>
> I was called in as an outside consultant and came up with a "quick-fix" that saved the day for them.
>
> After things fired up I stayed around as an interested observer, to catch the very beginning of our Space Exploration activity. That was somewhere back in the sixties. ...

A large team of IBM technicians was present to debug the system and get it running. No one really knew much except that it looked O.K. on paper.

It was during that time that I heard about the aberration in the location of the Heavenly bodies that led to the Bible account of how the MISSING DAY incident came about.

I was not the one who came up with the Bible answer, nor do I know the names of those involved. I simply reported it as it came to me and used it in my lectures on the Bible and Science, which I frequently deliver in schools and Colleges in Science Seminars.

A Newspaper reporter in Spencer, Indiana [Mary Kathryn Bryan in 1970] came across a copy, and fed it into the major News Services. To date I have received over 10,000 letters from all parts of the world.[44]

Many have correctly pointed out that computers do not stop "and put up a red flag."[45] Some have reported that Hill has retracted his story, but that is not true. Hill still maintains its veracity even though NASA has disavowed any and all knowledge of him, and others have charged him with various degrees of fraud. It has also been suggested that Hill had based the story on Totten's book,[46] but Hill claims not to have known of the Totten book at the time.[47] However, the main problem with Hill's story is that it would require an independent date for some event such as an eclipse of the sun prior to Joshua's long day. The most ancient of these observations does not go back as far as 1,000 B.C., let alone 1,500 B.C. Still, Hill's story raised quite a bit of interest.

A second computer account of a missing day appeared in the Swedish *Goteborgs Tidningen* on March 15, 1981. According to that story, Stig Flodmark of the University of Stockholm had discovered that the earth's axis had flipped on May 3, 1375 B.C. and associated that with Joshua's long day. This proposal is the same as that of Rand who was mentioned earlier in this chapter. According to Flodmark, an Ugaritic astronomer described the event and gave the date. Flodmark refers to a book entitled *Tidal Friction and the Earth's Rotation*.[48] The comment by the author of the quoted paper, F. R. Stephenson, in summarizing the Ugaritic observation, is "Sun put to shame; went down in daytime." This hardly describes a tippie top phenomenon, especially with Gibeon at the rotational north pole for the day, for the sun would have been circumpolar for the Ugaritic astronomer; it would not have gone "down in daytime."

Related Verses

Joshua 10:13 does not stand alone in the Bible. There are several similar verses. One of those is found in Habakkuk 3:11 which states:

> The sun and moon stood still in their habitation: at the light of thine arrows they went, and at the shining of thy glittering spear.

Now Habakkuk 3:11 is a double reference: in the first instance, it refers to a future event foreseen by Habakkuk; and in the second instance, it refers back to the taking of Canaan, back to Joshua's long day. As such, we may consider it as a unit with Joshua 10.

An apparent prophetic reference to Joshua's long day is found in Job 9:7 which seems to foretell the events described in Joshua 10. It is evident that Job was most likely a contemporary of Abraham or, at least, Job lived no later than Joseph or his sons.[49] The verse reads as follows:

> [God] commandeth the sun, and it riseth not; and sealeth up the stars.

The Date of Joshua's Long Day

We noted that the entry into the promised land was early April of 1448 B.C. Can we ascertain the month and day of Joshua's long day with any degree of certainty? It turns out that we can come close.

When the Israelites entered the promised land it was the tenth day of the first month (Joshua 4:19), shortly before the time of the Passover which is at the time of the full moon. Now in 1448 B.C. the new moon and the first day of spring closely coincided, the first day of spring being March 19.5 at the time;[50] so we can date the very entry into the promised land as Thursday, March 29, give or take a day.

The events, which are described between the Passover and the battle at Gibeon all, took time. The Passover celebration itself took a week; the fall of Jericho took seven days; the fall of Ai took at least four days; the construction of the altar on mount Ebal and the copying of the law probably took a week or more; the trickery of the Gibeonites took still more time; the communication of that trickery to the Gibeonites' neighbors and the subsequent formation of an alliance, not to mention their march to Gibeon, all took time. It is not unreasonable to assume that over a month passed between the celebration of the Passover and Joshua's long day. This is entirely consistent with the geometry of sun and moon presented in Joshua 10 where the moon seems to be west of the sun and both visible in daylight. Given that the time for the event was 9:00 a.m., the moon was most likely near or after its last quarter. More specifically, then, it appears that Joshua's long day happened somewhere between May 8 to May 15 of 1448 B.C.

The Commentators Concluded

It should be painfully clear by this time that not only was Joshua's long day a real miracle, but also it presents man with a great problem: either God writes what he means and means what he writes, or he does not. Most Christian scholars over the centuries have been of the opinion that God needs them to make his truth known, that God is incapable of explaining certain matters to man without that help. This is why most churches hold tradition over the authority of the Bible. Joshua 10:12-14 strikes at the heart of this heresy.

In the twelfth verse it can be argued that when Joshua spoke, he was simply ignorant of the rotation of the earth and thus accused the sun and moon of moving. Hence he spoke geocentrically. This would not introduce an error in the Bible since this is a direct quote. All that inerrancy requires is that the quote must be an accurate quote. That's fine and well for Joshua, but what of the thirteenth verse? Who is the writer who reports that the "sun stood still, and the moon stayed?" The Bible says that God is its author through the Holy Ghost (2 Timothy 3:16). Verses 13 and 14 of Joshua 10 present us with the point of view of the author, and the author is God himself. God cannot lie, so this point of view must be true. If the perspective is not true, then either God is lying or someone else inspired the wording. If the author is not God then who is he? And just what is that person doing putting words in God's mouth? If this verse cannot be trusted, then how can we trust any other Bible passage? Could not the same shadow of doubt be cast onto any other particular passage of scripture? And what, then, becomes of the Bible's witness of itself in such passages as 2 Timothy 3:16-17? Or if the commentator is God himself, is he speaking phenomenologically or anthropocentrically? Or is that impossible?

For the moment, let us assume that God is speaking either anthropocentrically or phenomenologically. Let us further suppose that this is not the only place in the Bible where God does so but that, in particular, he does so in all geocentric passages. Then what does that mean? Just what does it mean to speak *anthropocentrically* or *phenomenologically*?

Anthropocentrism literally means "man-centeredness." In this view God puts himself in man's place and speaks from a human perspective. Given that the Word became flesh and dwelt among us, this is not at all far-fetched, but does this really excuse the God of Truth, who is the Truth, from writing the whole truth and nothing but the truth? God forbid! Note how simply God could have avoided the contradiction between heliocentrism and geocentricity if instead he had started the thirteenth verse with: "And the earth stopped its turning ...." God does not go out of his way to avoid difficult wording just for the sake of simplicity (Proverbs 1:22). Nor does He express the science of the Bible in simple terms. Take Job chapter 38, for example, where two or three "puzzling" and "poetic" passages have in recent years been found to be literally true; yet most of the chapter is completely above man's comprehension. Simply put, God does not speak anthropocentrically because God is not a man.

Phenomenology is a science which deals with appearances rather than with actual existence (the study of the latter is called *ontology*). Phenomenology is based on the observation that appearances can be deceiving. Thus when one claims that Joshua 10:13 is *phenomenological*, one effectively claims that God is not presenting the situation as it *actually* is but only presents it as it *appears to be*. If the appearance is not the same as actual fact, then in the final analysis God is not relaying accurate information about the situation. For the sake of "convenience," God wrote an untruth. God presented the appearance of the situation as the truth rather than presenting the truth as the truth: this is what one means when one says that the Bible speaks *phenomenologically*.

Phenomenological or anthropocentric: either the sun stood still or the earth stood still; either God inerrantly inspired the wording or He did not; either the Bible is trustworthy or it is not. There is no middle ground. There is no room for compromise. After all, both the anthropocentric theory of inspiration and the phenomenological-language theory are forms of *accommodation* where God is said to accommodate his wording to the understanding of the common man. Good though that may sound on the surface, accommodation still maintains that God goes along with the accepted story even though he really does not believe it.

The whole issue would be moot if, as the liberals and infidels claim, the Bible was written by men and not God. Belief in the human authorship of Bible earmarked the Sadducees in Christ's day and still earmarks their spiritual descendants, the liberals, today. The Pharisees recognized the truth about the authorship of the Bible but failed to live up to that fact. When confronted by the truth of their hypocrisy they became enraged rather than repentant.

Today's Pharisee is no different, reacting with violent rage when confronted by these matters. Still, let God be true and every man a liar.

Putting it all Together

When it is all put together, we know more about Joshua's long day than we know of most other events recorded in the Bible. The best date seems to be within four or five days either side of May 12, 1448 B.C., sometime between 8:30 and 9:30 a.m. This we may conclude from plotting all of the long day, long night, and the long sunset accounts on a globe. Such extensive observations preclude the conclusion that the event was an optical illusion restricted to the land of Israel. It also disallows the notion that Joshua's long day is fictitious, for the testimony of the peoples around the world is entirely consistent with its reality. That some peoples have tales of a long night while others tell of a long day while none have both a long day and a long night tale signifies that Joshua's long day is not one account, originating in the mid-East, which has migrated all over the world; for if such were the case, then all nations would tell of a long day and none would tell of a long night, let alone a perfectly-placed long sunset. So we must conclude that Joshua's long day was a real, historical event and not some fiction.

Why, despite the testimonies of various peoples around the globe to the reality of an extremely long day or night, and despite the geographic consistency of the data in terms of day and night, why should the majority of scholars dismiss this wealth of evidence as mere superstition? How could there be more substantial evidence? On the other hand, we shall have occasion to document examples where modern science has accepted the testimony of one individual of dubious integrity. Actually, the heliocentric/geocentric debate is not new, nor is it secret, but the stakes are high and rarely mentioned; for authority is itself at stake. Just who is authoritative and in what? If doubt can be cast on the Bible as an authority in the area of science, then that leaves scientists as the final authority in that area. All too often science is merely another form of politics with little regard for truth if the truth be not expedient. Thus it can be said quite literally that today's science is tomorrow's superstition. That was as true in the sixth century B.C. as it is true today.

Witness Galileo Galilei, an early and vocal proponent of heliocentrism and regarded by many as the first true physicist. In 1613 he wrote in a letter to Castelli why Joshua's long day should not be believed:

And first I ask the adversary if he knows by what motions the sun is moved? If he does know, he must reply that it is moved with two motions, that is, an annual motion from west to east and an opposite diurnal motion from east to west. Hence, in the second place, I ask if these two movements, so diverse and almost contrary to one another, both belong to the sun and are equally its own? They are forced to answer no; that one alone is its own and particular motion, which is the annual, while the other is not the sun's at all, but that of the highest sky, called the Prime Mobile, which sweeps along with itself the sun and the other planets and also the starry sphere, constraining them to make one revolution around the earth in 24 hours, with a motion (as I said) almost contrary to their natural and proper motions.

So I come to the third question, and ask them by which of these two motions the sun produces day and night, that is, by its own or from the Prime Mobile? It is necessary to respond that day and night are the effects of motion of the Prime Mobile, while from the proper motion of the sun not day and night, but the different seasons, and the year itself are produced.

Now if the day depends not on the sun's motion, but on that of the Prime Mobile, who can fail to see that in order to prolong the day it is necessary to stop the Prime Mobile, and not the sun? ... It being therefore absolutely impossible, in the arrangement of Ptolemy and Aristotle, to stop the motion of the sun and to lengthen the day, as the Scripture affirms to have happened.[51]

In his challenge Galileo sets up a straw man and thus exemplifies the ignorance of the Bible which is so characteristic of humanity. True, if one ascribes the annual motion to the sun and the diurnal (daily) motion to the stars, then Galileo's argument is correct; but the Bible does not fall into such simple traps.

The Bible clearly indicates that the sun is to rule the day. This means that the daily motion is unique to the sun and has nothing to dowith the annual motion. The sun's period is exactly 24 hours. The stars' daily motion nearly matches the sun's period, being about 3 minutes 56 seconds less than the sun's period. Over the course of one year this amounts to one extra revolution about the earth, namely, the annual effect. (The north-south annual motion of the sun can be shown to be due to the difference between the sun's period of revolution and the rotation rate of the rest of the universe.) When viewed from that perspective, Galileo's argument falls flat on its face. Both motions are from east to west, but the sun's motion is roughly 1/365th slower than that of the cosmos. Thus the motions are not "almost contrary" but are almost identical. Yet no theologian has ever come up with a better argument against Joshua's long day than has Galileo at this one point.

Conclusion

The upshot is that there appears to be solid evidence from the Bible and from folklore around the world that there was one day which, depending upon geographical location, presented the inhabitants of the earth with an unusually long span of daylight or night. Attempts to explain this phenomenon by naturalistic means have all failed because no mechanism known to physics can absorb the earth's spin energy and momentum (or the universe's from a geocentric point of view) in such a short period of time without causing great upheavals such as the oceans spilling over the continents. Agnostic or atheistic scholars choose not to deal with the ancient witnesses. Such a phenomenon as Joshua's long day can only happen with divine intervention. But then science does not claim to have all the answers: its authority is found wanting. Is the

Bible, then, the final authority after all? Not if God said that the sun stopped when it was *actually* the earth which ceased to rotate. And that brings us to the heart of the matter.

Attempts to phenomenalize Joshua's long day or to make it allegorical thus fail. Christians and Jewish people are presented with a real historical event in Joshua 10:12-14. The central issue from their perspective is that of inerrancy of the Bible. God wrote in verse 13 that the "sun stood still and the moon stayed." God either meant what he wrote, or he did not. There is no excuse for God because he is the God of truth; therefore all things he says and does must reflect that fact. So God cannot utter an untruth and we must conclude that the Bible teaches, in Joshua 10:13 and elsewhere, that the universe rotates around the earth once per day, carrying the sun, moon and stars with it, regardless of what introductory astronomy texts may say. We shall see later that the advanced texts belie the introductory texts on the matter of the rotation of the earth. For the time being, the choice is either the Bible or the introductory astronomy texts: which do you believe?

Figure 2: (next page) *Joshua's long day around the world.*

Open circles map accounts of a long day
Dark circles map accounts of a long night
The triangle locates the account of a long sunset.

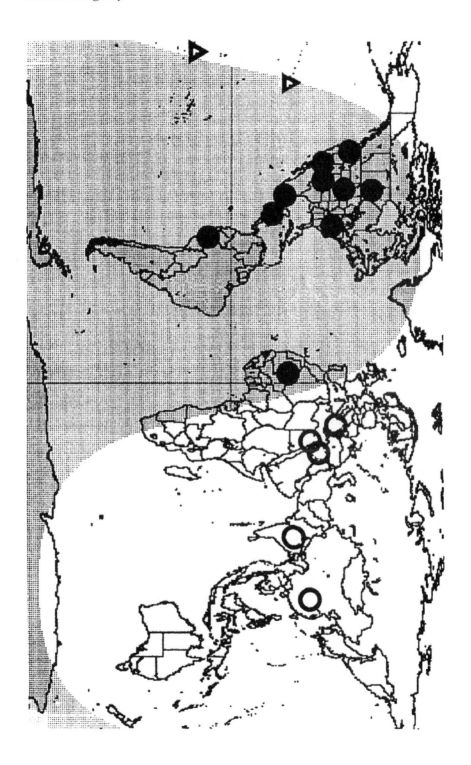

A similar figure can be constructed for Hezekiah's sign (see page 32). The locations not only show the time of day, but even the time of year for Hezekiah's sign. The time of year is ascertained within a week. Clearly, neither Hezekiah's sign nor Joshua's Long Day can be dismissed as events local to Israel. They are demonstrably global events.

> The story of Christianity tells about a plan
> of salvation centered upon a particular
> people and a particular man. As long as
> someone is thinking in terms of a geocen-
> tric universe and an earth-deity, the story
> has a certain plausibility.

> — A. J. Burgess[1]

6

CHRISTOLOGICAL SUN PASSAGES

The scriptures speak of the promised Messiah, the Christ, the Anointed One who is to come to earth to redeem a people unto himself. The Bible leaves no room for doubt but that the Messiah is Jehovah incarnate. The Bible uses several symbols for the Messiah such as the "Branch" and the "Lamb of God." The Messiah is also referred to as the "Sun" or the "Sun of righteousness." In this chapter and the next, we consider those verses which tie the sun and Messiah together. But first, let's examine the significance of the issue.

The Significance of Geocentricity to Christology

The chapter quote by Burgess touches the issue which was crucial in the humanists' fight for heliocentrism and against the churches during the sixteenth and seventeenth centuries. Burgess later expounds on it by continuing with:

> As soon as astronomy changes theories, however, the whole
> Christian history loses the only setting within which it
> would make sense. With the solar system no longer the

center of anything, imagining that what happens here forms the center of a universal drama becomes simply silly.[2]

Thus the vanquishing of the geocentric theory in favor of heliocentrism is perceived by many as the death knell of Christianity; and is it any wonder? For the earth is truly central in the purpose of the mind of God throughout the scriptures. Furthermore, of the symbols used to represent the "particular man" who is the focus of history, some of those symbols are geocentric and none are heliocentric. If these symbols are in error, then how may one trust the framework of scripture?

Consider Psalm 84:11 for an example of a passage where Christ is identified with the sun:

> For the LORD God is a sun and shield: the LORD will give grace and glory: no good thing will he withhold from them that walk uprightly.

Many there are who hold that Jesus Christ is not the LORD God and that this verse, as a result, is not Christological; but besides this verse, the Messiah is called *The Mighty God* in Isaiah 9:6 as well as several other places such as Revelation 1:8. (Note verse 18 there – when did the Almighty die if Christ was not the Almighty?) Thence we must include this passage as Christological.

Psalm 19

One crucial geocentric Christological sun reference occurs in the first six verses of Psalm 19.

[1] The heavens declare the glory of God; and the firmament sheweth his handywork.
[2] Day unto day uttereth speech, and night unto night sheweth knowledge.
[3] There is no speech nor language where their speech is not heard.

⁴ Their line is gone out through all the earth, and their words to the end of the world. In them hath he set a tabernacle for the sun,
⁵ which is as a bridegroom coming out of his chamber, and rejoiceth as a strong man to run a race.
⁶ His going forth is from the end of heaven, and his circuit unto the ends of it: and there is nothing hid from the heat thereof.

The first four verses speak of the heavens while verses 4b through 6 speak of the sun in heaven. These correspond respectively to verses 7 through 10, which speak of the scriptures and with verses 11 through 14, which speak of Jesus in the scriptures. The heavens are associated with the scriptures and the sun is associated with Jesus. Note that it is the sun that moves about the earth (verse 6).

Although too many commentators maintain that the nineteenth Psalm is actually a fusion of two unrelated psalms, note that the Lord Jesus Christ is the connecting thread throughout the Psalm. At least one of his attributes is reflected in every single verse of the Psalm. In the first verse he is present as the Creator, in the second as the Revelator, in the third as the Word, in the fourth as the Light, in the fifth as Bridegroom, in the sixth as the Judge, in the seventh as the Lawgiver, in the eighth as Healer, in the ninth as the Eternal One, in the tenth as the Pearl of Great Price for the believer, in the eleventh as Prophet, in the twelfth as the Atonement for sin, in the thirteenth as Savior, and in the fourteenth as Redeemer. If this Psalm is errant in any way, then can there be a perfect salvation? Even the seventh verse testifies that "the testimony of the LORD is pure"; and we know that God's word is eternally settled in heaven (Psalm 119:89).

The sixth verse is eminently Christological. The motion of the sun is there linked to the emergence of the bridegroom. Furthermore, the reference to the sun's heat speaks of the judgment. The Authorized Bible starts the verse with the personal pronoun, "his," thus reinforcing the type of the bridegroom and also the Christology of the verse. Modern versions start this verse with "its" and thus deny the person of Christ as being evident in this verse and so deny that the sun is a type of Christ in this passage. The sun's circuit (verse 6) takes it around the zodiac, yearly tracing the gospel as told in the stars: starting from the nativity (Virgo) to the sacrificial death, resurrection, and final triumph as the Lion of Judah which is reflected in the constellation of Leo, the lion.

Ends of Heaven

Because of the evident Christology of Psalm 19, we should expect it to receive more than the usual amount of criticism. In verse six the second and third English words are "going forth." This is actually one Hebrew word, *motsa*. Modern versions use the word "rising" instead of "going forth" even though *motsa* is never used to mean "rise." *Motsa* always means "go forth." The closest that *motsa* ever comes to meaning "rise" is to "well up" like a spring or fountain. It is never used for a sunrise anywhere or anytime.

Psalm 19:6 starts with the clause: "His going forth is from the end of the heaven." Ofttimes commentators are confused by this phraseology because to many, it appears to mean that the sun has to traverse from one spatial end of heaven to the other. This affords the liberal reinforcement for his idea that the Bible envisions a small universe with a sun, circling the earth, fastened to or moving along a perimeter or "end" of heaven. But there is more to the universe than space, for there is also time. Indeed, the simple reading of the phrase would indicate that time, not space, is meant; for how else can one measure the "going forth," especially since heaven is here described as having more than one end and a circle has no end? But note how Psalm 19:6 ties in with the end of the heaven as foretold in Revelation 6:14 where we read:

> And the heaven departed as a scroll when it is rolled together; and every mountain and island were moved out of their places.

The significance of this departure of the heaven is given in the seventeenth verse:

For the great day of his wrath is come; and who shall be able to stand?

Revelation 6:14 thus speaks of the end of the heaven, one of the very ends of which Psalm 19:6 speaks. Indeed, the going forth of the Bridegroom is exactly heralded by the end of the heaven as described in Revelation 6:14. The other end of heaven would, by contrast, be its beginning or the end of its creation which corresponds to the creation of the sun on the fourth day.

The word "circuit" as it appears in verse six can mean one of two things in English. First, it can mean a *closed* path and second, it can designate an area of legal jurisdiction. The same two meanings are tied together in the Hebrew word here translated as "circuit" in the Authorized Bible. Hence, the verse refers to both meanings and insofar as it speaks of judgment, we find the next clause, "and there is nothing hid from the heat thereof," to be in agreement with the New Testament teaching that the present universe will be destroyed with fervent heat.

Circuit of the Sun

The geocentric import of Psalm 19:6 lies in the fact that the sun, not the earth, is described as moving. More specifically, the sun is said to be moving in a circuit, not circuits. The word "circuit" means a real or imaginary line described in going around any area. Heliocentrists have argued that since the distance from earth to sun is relatively small in comparison to the size of the universe, the circuit referred to here could not possibly refer to the motion of the sun around the earth since such a short distance cannot be described as anywhere approaching the size indicated by the "ends" of heaven. Now we have just dealt with that issue, but heliocentrists further maintain that the motion of the sun about the galactic center (the center of the Milky Way) is what is being referred to in verse six by the word "circuit." But this ignores the fact that the orbit of the sun about the galactic center, relative to the scale of the universe, is not much larger than the earth-sun distance they objected to earlier. One cannot escape the geocentricity of the verse by any such argument of scale.

If, however, one assumes the heliocentrists' interpretation that Psalm 19:6 refers to the motion of the sun about the center of the Galaxy, then a new set of problems arises. First, the passage refers to the circuit of the sun; and according to the dictionary, a circuit is a closed path. In order for the path of the sun about the galactic center to be referred to as a "circuit," the universe must be old enough to allow for its closure. Thus either these are the last days and the universe is at least 250 million years old (the time it takes the sun to orbit the galactic center once); or we are 6,000 years into a 250-million-year journey before the return of Christ. This is a special problem for those who insist both that the universe is about 6,000 years old and who proffer a galactocentric interpretation for Psalm 19:6.

A second problem with the galactocentric interpretation of Psalm 19:6 lies in the fact that the sun's orbit about the galactic center is not closed. Because of that, the sun's path about the center of the Milky Way cannot be referred to as a "circuit." The pretty picture of all the planets orbiting the sun in paths that close upon themselves works somewhat for planets, but it does not at all work for stars in a galaxy. Figure 3 illustrates a typical orbit for a star in a galaxy. As seen from above, the orbit appears to be closed although neither elliptical nor circular in shape; but in actual fact, the sun also bobs up and down out of the plane of the galaxy with a period of about 32 million years that is not the same as the 250-million-year period of revolution. Hence when the path appears to cross, the sun is at different heights relative to the galactic plane (above or below the paper). So the sun's galactic orbit can never be said to "enclose an area" and could never be considered to be a "circuit." And so the Bible is either wrong in using "circuit," or the Bible is referring to some motion other than that of the sun about the galactic center.

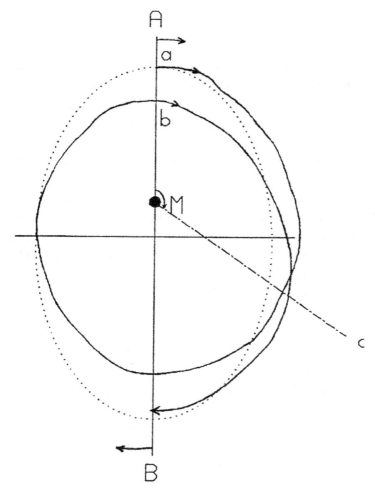

Figure 3: *Galactocentric orbit*

The dotted line traces out a standard 250-million-year orbit about the center of the Milky Way, *M.* In actuality, if the sun were to start at *a*, it follows a path more like that traced by the solid line. Technically, the orbit is complete at *b*, but note there that the sun has not described a closed path and so has not completed a "circuit." This is so for two reasons: first, the line *AB* rotates (to point *c* during the sun's orbit) and also the sun "bobs" up and down out of the plane of the galaxy with a period of 32 million years. Additionally, the sun's path varies erratically as it has "close" (several light years) encounters with neighboring stars and passes through the mass-concentrations of the spiral arms and clouds of dust and gas.

To illustrate the third problem we ask, "What is so special about the galactic center as a reference frame?" The heliocentrist must answer: "Nothing." As far as modern astronomy is concerned, the galactic center is every bit as arbitrary a frame of reference as is the placement of the sun (or earth) at the center of the universe. Furthermore, it would seem that the Galaxy is itself orbiting some as yet vaguely recognized point in a local group of galaxies. Why not pick that center? But this obscures the word "circuit" even more.

Now an astute reader may already have objected that by the same token the sun's daily motion about the earth may not necessarily close upon itself either, so that the term "circuit" would be equally inapplicable in the geocentric case. It is indisputable that the distance from the earth to the sun varies through the course of the year. For about six months of the year, the sun moves away from the earth; and for the remainder of the year, it moves toward the earth. The size of this to-and-fro motion is about three million miles, but the diameter of the sun is 886,000 miles which is less than one third the size of the overall to-and-fro motion. Since all this motion happens in a time span of 12 months, it takes six months to cover 3 million miles. In a geocentric sense where the sun goes around the earth once a day, we see that there is plenty of overlap; that at least a fifth of the volume of space the sun is currently passing through will also be inside the sun 24 hours from now. So the variability of the earth-sun distance cannot be said to deny the validity of the word "circuit" in Psalm 19:6 if the diurnal motion of the sun about the earth is meant by the text.

The sun's to-and-fro motion relative to the earth is not the only geocentric motion which the sun describes, however. Throughout the course of the year, the sun also moves in a path from north to south and back again (Figure 4). The sun moves a 23.5-degree span in the course of a quarter year or about 91 days. When crossing the equator the sun is moving at its fastest rate in the north-south direction. At that time it is moving northward (or southward) at 0.37 degree per day. This is very close to the angular diameter of the sun which is 0.48 degree. Yet, when we take into account both to-and-fro motion as well as the north-south motion, we find that the sun's path (or *world-line*) overlaps at least 17 percent between successive diurnal passages. In other words, even under the most adverse conditions, of all the space through which the sun passes at a particular instant, 17 percent of that same space will be found within the sun 24 hours later and a different 17 percent would have been found within the sun 24 hours earlier. This means that **only** in a geocentric system is the daily motion of the sun about the earth describable by the term "circuit," since only in a geocentric framework, where the earth is not moving through space, is the orbit of the sun "closed." Thus the term "circuit," as used in Psalm 19:6 is only strictly true if the sun goes around the earth once in a day; otherwise God made another poor, unfortunate choice of words in Psalm 19:6.

All things considered, no one has yet come up with a scientifically and hermeneutically "acceptable" apologetic for Psalm 19:6 in a heliocentric framework. The passage remains both Christological and geocentric.[3]

Isaiah 13:10

The nineteenth Psalm is not the only place in scripture where Christ is compared to the sun. Another such passage is Isaiah 13:10 where we again encounter the phrase "his going forth" with reference to the sun:

> For the stars of heaven and the constellations thereof shall not give their light: the sun shall be darkened in his going forth, and the moon shall not cause her light to shine.

The setting of this verse is the time of the judgment. It describes a time when the Lord shall hide himself in thick darkness. The sun, in consistent typology, is also darkened. It is the time when "he who now letteth" will be taken out of the way (2 Thessalonians 2:7).

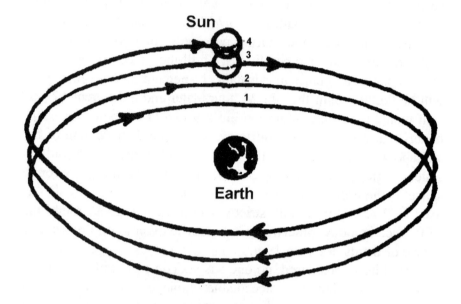

Figure 4: *The sun's daily circuit spiral*
Shown over the course of three days

One may argue that Isaiah 13:10 refers to the course of the sun through space, and certainly if this passage stood alone one could not refute such an argument. But we must keep in mind that this passage does not stand alone; contextually, it goes along with other passages such as Psalm 19:6. The point is that this verse describes the sun as moving and indicates that the sun's motion has been going on for some time. Again, given the Christology of the verse, Revelation 6:14 comes to mind. (See Revelation 7.) It should also be borne in mind that if Christ came in undimmed glory, the intensity of that infinite Light would consume the earth with its very heat (Psalm 19:6).

Judges 5:31

Still another biblical reference to the "going forth" of the sun is found in Judges 5:31 where we read:

So let all thine enemies perish, O LORD: but let them that love him be as the sun when he goeth forth in his might.

This verse is found in the song of Deborah and Barak and has obvious Christological overtones. The pronouns "him," "he," and "his" all refer to Christ. Here, too, the point is that the sun is described as moving. One could, of course, argue that Deborah and Barak are speaking from a human perspective and thus speak phenomenologically. This argument would appear to do no particular violence to God's literary prowess since he would simply be reporting the facts, namely, quoting what the two judges of Israel said without endorsing the truth thereof. Questions about inspired quotes and allied Christology aside, this argument does not work with the narrative voice such as found in Isaiah 13:10.

Malachi 4:2

The final Christological sun passage which we shall consider is the one that is most obviously Messianic in import and that is Malachi 4:2–

But unto you that fear my name shall the Sun of righteousness arise with healing in his wings; and ye shall go forth, and grow up as calves of the stall.

The context is the destruction of the wicked at the time of the judgment of believers. The verse itself points to the start of the millennium; to the first resurrection as opposed to the second resurrection which occurs at the end of the millennium. But there is an even broader implication in the verse.

In Malachi 4:2 the Sun is said to do the rising, not the earth doing the turning toward the sun as modern astronomy would have it. This reflects Christ's resurrection from the tomb at sunrise Jerusalem time. And so it is that if the sun does not truly "rise" (that is, move), that the typology is destroyed in both Malachi 4:2 and Psalm 19:6. It makes the resurrection only "apparent" or "phenomenological." The typology of the sun as moving fits perfectly with the biblical teaching that Christ came and will come again and that we do not go to him. In short, if the Bible speaks phenomenologically or figuratively when it says that the sun "arose," then how can we, as believers, require that it presents a literal truth in reporting that the Son "arose"? To challenge the validity of the word "rise" in any part of scripture is to challenge its validity in all parts, most particularly in the resurrection.

Is Geocentricity Figurative in the Bible?

Finally, although it has no direct bearing upon the geocentricity of the verse, we must consider the reference to the wings of Christ as present in Malachi 4:2. Heliocentrists have widely argued that if the motions of the sun are to be taken literally in the Bible that things like God's face, hands, arms, feet, legs, breast, and wings must also be taken literally. Augustine went so far as to utterly condemn all those who believe that God has actual hands and feet. Yet in the Old Testament God's wings alone are referred to no fewer than ten times, not to mention numerous references throughout the Bible where God is said to have human features. Take John's description of the Almighty in Revelation 1:8 as an example. Can there be room for doubt that God has a man-like figure when the Bible reports "one like unto the Son of man"? The thirteenth verse equates that man-like form with the Almighty God. Those who argue that it is blasphemy to believe that God has hands and feet, let alone wings, maintain this position on the grounds that John 4:24 teaches that God is a spirit and then add, without biblical support, that a spirit has no form. In particular they claim that in Luke 24:39, Jesus says that a spirit does not have flesh and bones. Jesus does not say that a spirit has no form but on the contrary, the very wording he chose ("a spirit hath not flesh and bones as ye see me have") indicates that a spirit does have form and hence, by implication, has hands and feet. In 1 Samuel 28:14, too, the spirit of Samuel is not only recognizable as the form of an old man; but he is even described as covered with a mantle.

Zechariah 12:1 explicitly teaches that a spirit has form for there it is recorded that:

> The burden of the LORD for Israel, saith the LORD, which stretcheth forth the heavens, and layeth the foundation of the earth, and formeth the spirit of man within him.

Clearly, if God "forms" man's spirit, then man's spirit must have a form or else the text is useless.

Given these arguments and passages, how can anyone assume that a spirit has no form? Likewise, given the wealth of references to God's bodily parts, how can one maintain that God does not have hands and feet or even wings? Is anything too hard for the Lord? Most assuredly, God has hands and feet. His hands and feet bear the nail prints of Calvary. As for his wings, Malachi 4:2 tells that these will only be seen by believers, those that "fear my name," those who have the Holy Ghost dwelling within them. After all, doves have wings, don't they?

> ... and he saw the Spirit of God descending like a dove, and lighting upon him (Matthew 3:16).

Can there be any doubt as to the nature of the "healing in his wings"?

Conclusion

The Bible makes a special point to use the sun as a type for Jesus, the Messiah. In every case, the sun does the moving as a type of Christ moving from heaven to earth for our sakes. But if we are to assume, as heliocentrists insist, that the word "rise" when applied to the *sun* is not to be taken literally, then how can we insist that the application of the same word to the *Son* must be taken literally? Thus we are forced to the conclusion that to cast doubt on the geocentric biblical model for the universe, is to cast doubt upon the very resurrection of the Lord Jesus Christ.

The sun was risen upon the earth
when Lot entered into Zoar.

— Genesis 19:23

7

SUNRISE AND SUNSET

B y far the most numerous passages overtly speaking of the daily
motion of the sun about the earth are those which refer to sunrise or sunset. Embedded in these very words is the idea that the
sun does the rising and the setting and that the earth is but a pas-
sive participant in the process. We shall not examine these passages in any great detail. There is no need for that. The geocentricity implicit in the words "sunrise" and "sunset" is universally
acknowledged.

Statistical Occurrences

All the occurrences of the words "sunrise" and "sunset" can be
grouped into five categories.

The first of the five categories lists 26 references where the
sun is referred to as either "going down" or "setting."

In the second category there are 30 references. Each of these
refers to the sun as "rising."

The third category is not overtly geocentric in nature. It includes those verses which speak of the sun as "being down" but
which do not speak of the sun as having moved in order to be

down. We include these because it is explicit in the first two cases that the sun does the moving and the third case states the result of that motion.

Likewise, the fourth category does not directly mention the sun as moving. It lists all the verses where the sun is referred to as "being up."

Finally, the fifth category speaks of the position of the earth relative to the sun. In a sense, this category is strictly geocentric for geocentricity only secondarily involves the immobility of the earth, but it primarily means that the earth is located at the reference center of the universe. This means that the cardinal directions, including up and down, must refer to the earth. Category five thus lists all those Bible passages which use the phrase "under the sun." Given that the sun moves around the earth once a day, the phrase "under the sun" of necessity dictates that the earth is located at the origin of God's frame of reference; that is, in a central position and thus indicative of geocentricity.

Statistically, the phrase "under the sun" occurs 30 times in the Bible, all of them in the book of Ecclesiastes. The word "sun" appears 159 times in addition to 10 occurrences of the word "sunrising." Of these 169 references, 30 occur in the aforementioned phrase, "under the sun." Of the remaining 139 solar references, 57 are overtly indicative of the motion of the sun and another 9 indirectly point to the sun's diurnal motion. Additionally, there are those verses, like Psalm 19:6 which we referred to earlier in chapter 6, which speak of the sun as "going forth." These have not been tallied in the sunrise/sunset passages. All in all, well over half the references to the sun are geocentric in nature.

Key Verses

As an example of one of the sunrise/sunset passages, we consider Psalm 104:19 which is particularly strong as well as scientifically puzzling:

He appointed the moon for seasons: the sun knoweth his
going down.

The Christology is evident since the Bible makes it clear that the
Son (as typed by the sun) knows his "going down." Of course, this
refers not only to his imminent return but to his birth in a Bethlehem stable as well as his burial and subsequent descent into hell.
The scientific impact of this passage lies in the pronouncement that
somehow the sun "knoweth his going down." It is inadvisable to
dismiss this reference as poetic and thus without truth (for poetry is
every wit as truthful as prose) since, as man's knowledge increases,
the number of such "poetic" passages in the Bible is steadily decreasing. For the time being, however, the scientific connotation of
the verse must remain a mystery. In any case, how can the sun
know his going down if he is not "going down" but if the earth,
instead, is turning?

There is a second sunrise/sunset passage which we shall consider simply because it occupied a central place in the Renaissance
debates between geocentricity and heliocentrism. That passage is
the fifth verse in the first chapter of Ecclesiastes:

The sun also ariseth, and the sun goeth down, and hasteth to
his place where he arose.

In Ecclesiastes 1:5 we encounter the same reference to the burial and resurrection of Christ that we earlier encountered in Psalm
104:19. The verse is quite explicit in claiming that the sun is moving, for it even adds that he "hasteth." Certainly this verse is not
literally true if heliocentrism is true. Again, if the passage is not
true then in the final analysis, either God did not inspire it or else
God is a liar. Claiming that God did not inspire it makes him out
to be a liar anyhow for he claims authorship of all of these passages
in the context of 2 Timothy 3:16-17, which see.

Now there are those who claim that since the passages surrounding Ecclesiastes 1:5 cannot be taken literally, that Ecclesiastes
1:5 should not be taken literally either. This argument is actually a
leftover from the sixteenth and seventeenth century debates for

heliocentrism and it is now mindlessly parroted, for in the intervening centuries science has learned that these verses are literally true. We shall examine them if for no other reason than that said examination will serve as an example of the statement made earlier about the declining number of "poetic" passages in scripture.

The first verse is certainly literal enough:

The words of the Preacher, the son of David, king in Jerusalem.

The second verse is likewise literally true although its truth may not be immediately apparent:

Vanity of vanities, saith the Preacher, vanity of vanities; all is vanity.

The theological problem here lies with the term "all." Originally, the objection was that the word "all" if taken literally, would include the Lord God himself; but today we know that to be false. Mathematically, there is no such thing as "the set of all sets." That means that the set of all sets follows different rules than the individual sets making up that set of all sets. In other words, the infinite God is not part of the "all" referred to in Ecclesiastes 1:2. So mathematical understanding exempts God from being included in the "all" of the verse and thus he is not there branded as "vain." We do not have to speculate, as some have, as to whether or not Solomon was in or out of the "will of God." The second verse, in writing that all is vanity, writes a literal truth.

Next comes the third verse:

What profit hath a man from all his labor which he taketh under the sun?

Except perhaps for "under the sun," which is the point at issue, the question is quite literal and can be answered in a literal way.

The fourth verse was already discussed in Chapter 3:

One generation passeth away, and another generation cometh: but the earth abideth for ever.

That generations come and go seems literal enough. The only
problem one might have is with the earth "abiding for ever," but
that was covered before in Chapter 3.

Since the first four verses are literally true, then on that basis
there should be no problem with the truth of the fifth verse. But
what of the sixth verse? Perhaps the figurative part starts there:

The wind goeth toward the south, and turneth about unto
the north; it whirleth about continually, and the wind returneth again according to his circuits.

Not until the twentieth century did man finally come to realize this
verse is also literally true. In the northern hemisphere's temperate
zone (where most of the world's people live), the prevailing winds
blow from west to east. In addition to this the wind moves from
north to south on a slower but also much grander scale. Along the
surface of the earth's northern hemisphere the wind has a north-to-
south component while several miles above the ground it goes from
south to north. Additionally, depending upon whether the air is
massed into a high-pressure area or a low-pressure area, air cir-
culates in counter-clockwise or clockwise direction. Termed
cyclones and *anticyclones*, these circulating masses of air all attest
to the literal truth of this verse even though the rotational directions
are reversed in the southern hemisphere. Now the wind is a type of
the Holy Ghost and that typology is evident in the sixth verse where
"his circuits" alludes to Christ, the Holy Ghost being available only
through Christ's sacrificial death on the cross and his resurrection.

We could go on to show the literal truth of every verse in the
chapter, but we shall conclude with the seventh verse which is also
of scientific import:

All the rivers run into the sea; yet the sea is not full; unto
the place from whence the rivers come, thither they return
again.

At the time that Solomon penned these words it is doubtful that man knew much about convection, condensation, and evaporation; yet here we have a scientifically accurate description of the water cycle. Rivers flow into the ocean and the water of the ocean evaporates only to be precipitated as rain, dew, hail, or snow upon the land. There the waters flow together into rivers which flow back to the ocean, starting the cycle all over again. Clearly, the seventh verse is a literal truth.

Contrary to the unthinking heliocentrists' claims, we see that Ecclesiastes 1:5 is surrounded by verses which are literally true. So the fifth verse cannot be shrugged off so easily as to suggest that it is embedded in verses which are all figurative and not literal.

At the Judgment

We now consider two more examples of sunrise/sunset passages. There are a number of biblical passages which deal with the state of the sun during the great tribulation and judgment. Job 9:7 is one such reference. In it we read that God:

> commandeth the sun, and it riseth not; and sealeth up the stars.

The prior verse gives the context as the time of God's wrath. The point here is that it is the sun, not the earth, which is commanded to stop. If the earth rotated then the earth should be commanded to stop, not the sun.

The second of the sunrise/sunset examples involving the tribulation and judgment is Habakkuk 3:11. The fifth through ninth verses set the stage for the eleventh verse which reads:

> The sun and moon stood still in their habitation: at the light of thine arrows they went, and at the shining of thy glittering spear.

This refers to an incident of which Joshua's long day is a type. Regardless of when one may wish to place this event, the fact remains that the sun and moon are described as standing still in their habitation, that is, in heaven (Psalm 19:4). Admittedly, this could be taken to mean that the sun's motion about the center of the Galaxy ceased (or will cease) as well as the moon's motion about the earth; but in light of all the previous passages which speak directly of the motions of the sun and moon around the earth, the geocentric interpretation is by far the most likely.

Linguistic Considerations

Finally, we look at the liberals' defense of heliocentrism versus the biblical doctrine of geocentricity. Evolutionary apologists have for centuries maintained that the words "sunrise" and "sunset" are the product of the evolution of language. They suppose the languages of the earth all stem from grunts and groans emitted in the remote past. Gradually, they claim, the languages became more and more complex. But this is not the view of the Bible. The scriptures teach that the world's languages came from one common language (probably Hebrew) which was *confounded* (not *confused*; there is a great difference between the two terms!) at the tower of Babel's construction site (Genesis 11:1-9).

Suffice it to say that the Bible's account seems far more realistic than the evolutionists' on the grounds of both the second law of thermodynamics (that things will degenerate in time) as well as historical observation; for we see the world's languages becoming *less* sophisticated in time, not more. Take English as an example. The subtle distinction between the words "throughly" and "thoroughly" has long been forgotten, yet the difference was considered crucial four hundred years ago.[1] Anyone who would take the trouble to find out just why the Authorized Bible used "odd" phraseology at times would soon be amazed at how much detail, explicitness, and fine structure the English language has lost in the last four hundred years. There is no language in the world which is naturally or evolutionarily improving. True, more and more words may be hybridized or absorbed from one language into another, but the sentence structures and parts of speech are fast losing distinctiveness.

If God, as the Bible teaches, created Adam's language as well as confounded the languages at Babel, then why did he not "naturally" accommodate them to accept the "truth" of heliocentrism? He gave us an innate capacity to understand things like colors and shapes; why could he not have done the same for the relative motions of the earth, sun, and stars? It would appear that the heliocentrists not only make God out to be a clumsy grammarian and sloppy in his typology, but he either cannot or will not even create a true language, a language which does not succumb to appearances over truth. God could have created and confounded the languages to accommodate the truth of heliocentrism, if truth it be.

Consider this example to show how very simple it would have been for God to have structured the English language so that it naturally includes heliocentrism. It may sound jarring to our ears, but the word "sunrise" would "more correctly" be "tosun," which would acknowledge that the rotation of the earth would carry one toward the sun at sunrise. Likewise, sunset could be called "fromsun" since at that time one moves away from the sun in a heliocentric framework. This is no more cryptic or unusual than, say, the word "replenish" which, though it is commonly thought to mean "refill," actually means "to fill in an already-existing environment, background or backdrop," especially with some divine intervention such as the newly created flora and fauna as we find in Genesis 1:28 or supernaturally-quickly-grown flora such as was found after the flood in Genesis 9:1. When it comes to the issue of heliocentrism, God either made the languages of the world to be phenomenological or else the sun really does go around the earth.

Conclusion

The Bible verses which speak of the rising of the sun and its setting afford us the largest bulk of passages directly supporting the biblical doctrine of geocentricity. Again the issue boils down to the same point we've noted in previous chapters. Either God meant what he wrote or he did not mean what he wrote and would, presumably, revise his original writing as well as write differently if he were to write today. And if he would recant today, then where is the truth?

The heliocentric theory, by putting the sun at the center of the universe, ... made man appear to be just one of a possible host of wanderers drifting through a cold sky. It seemed less likely that he was born to live gloriously and to attain paradise upon his death. Less likely, too, was it that he was the object of God's ministrations.

— Morris Kline[1]

8

THE THRONE

When the news of Copernicus' promotion of the belief that the earth orbits the sun reached the ears of the Reformers, they expressed their disapproval of the idea. Most notable of those was Martin Luther who expressed some anxiety about possible consequences of the theory if it should ever be accepted as true. Throughout the history of the debate between geocentricity and heliocentrism, Christian and Jewish theologians expressed a moral uneasiness about the decentralization of the earth.

Timing the Effects of Changes in Morality

After less than a couple of decades of heliocentrism, the heliocentrists started to argue that since no moral upset seemed in the offing, that the Biblicists must be wrong in their voicing of moral reservations against heliocentrism. But in that they were premature. Heliocentrism did not become the dominant opinion until about 1650, one hundred years after the publication of Copernicus' book which triggered the shift from geocentrism. Furthermore, history shows that it takes at least a generation for the long-term effects of a change in morality to manifest themselves. Changes in mores do not have immediate full impact on populations. Thus, to gauge the effect of heliocentrism we must look beyond the first generation which completely adopts it. We must look after 1650 to evaluate the impact of heliocentrism on morality. Only then can we see if the Reformers were correct in their moral trepidations about heliocentrism.

Just how such moral degeneration could result from such a subtle shift in worldview is not intuitively obvious. Nevertheless, the concern of the Reformers and other Christians has proven to be well founded; for heliocentrism directly spawned the view that man is but a mere machine, a cosmic accident. Heliocentrism is widely acknowledged as the foundation of the impersonal, mechanistic, materialistic universe and the existentialist view that human life is purposeless and thus, by implication, worthless. How this shift in moral outlook developed historically will be discussed in Part II of this book, but we have already noted its foundation in the quote by Burgess which heads Chapter 6, who correctly notes that Christianity without geocentricity is just plain "silly."

To understand the Reformers' uneasiness about heliocentrism we start at Isaiah 66:1 where we are told that the earth is the Lord's footstool:

> Thus saith the LORD, The heaven is my throne, and the earth is my footstool: where is the house that ye build unto me? and where is the place of my rest?

The theme of the earth as footstool is extended in Acts 7:49 (which is not a quote of Isaiah 66:1 but an elaboration):

> Heaven is my throne, and earth is my footstool: what house will ye build me? saith the Lord: or what is the place of my rest?

Note that the two places mentioned, heaven and earth, were the first things created (Genesis 1:1).

Moral Relativism

It is usual for thrones and footstools to be at rest relative to each another. As Professor James Hanson has put it: "Footstools are not footstools if they are moving." It is also usual for there to be some space between them. The Bible refers to the "room" in which these two items are found as a "habitation" and it does so on two occasions. The first of these is Psalm 89:14 where it is mentioned that:

> Justice and judgment are the habitation of thy throne: mercy
> and truth shall go before thy face.

The second occasion is Psalm 97:2 which adds:

> Clouds and darkness are round about him: righteousness
> and judgment are the habitation of his throne.

There are thus three things which the Bible singles out as constituting the habitation of the throne of God and those three are justice, judgment, and righteousness. The throne is not moving relative to these so these three elements of the throne's habitation are constant; they are absolute; they never change. Likewise, by the analogy of the footstool, these three elements are also not moving with respect to the earth if the earth is at rest relative to the outer heaven (God's throne). This means that the space between footstool and throne, the middle heaven, (outer space), must do the moving.

Notice what happens if we regard the earth as moving. Through the word of God, the earth sees the same three elements of the habitation of the throne; but since the earth is viewed as moving, the concepts of justice, judgment, and righteousness can be viewed as moving with it. Now this affords two conclusions. Either there are absolute moral standards which are universally true and which are not affected by the earth's motion so that they would only "appear" to accompany the earth in its dizzying path, or the standards can be viewed as part of the earth since they share its motions. This latter concept of morality makes moral precepts to be just another earthly fixture, like a mountain or a building. This is the twentieth century moral view. It allows one to conclude that the biblical moral norms are not absolutes but are culturally defined standards. From there it is only a small step to the conclusion that all morality is relative and that there are no moral absolutes. In other words, the modern existential concept of moral relativism is an inference drawn from belief in the earth's motion.

Now many may wish to invoke the omnipresence of God in order to reconcile a stable throne with a moving footstool, but those who do so must also confront the fact that God speaks in overtly geocentric tones throughout the entire Bible. And they must also confront the fact that God cannot lie, even for convenience's sake; for if God did ever utter a lie, then the creative power of His Word is so great that the "lie" would immediately come to pass.

The above reasoning relating heliocentrism to the philosophical concept of *moral relativism* may seem far-fetched to most, but there is additional support for the inference besides the comments of the Reformers. We shall explore this additional evidence in the final chapter of this book.

All this is not to say that there were no moral relativists before Copernicus, for clearly there have been such throughout all of history; but it is to say that moral relativists can claim less scientific support for their views from a geocentric framework than from a heliocentric world view.

The Plumbline[2]

If the earth is rotating, let alone the profusion of other superimposed motions, a plumbline at the Temple from the mercy seat would seldom, if ever, point to God's throne with New Jerusalem. Such a line, when seen from the throne, would aimlessly flail about. But in scripture, this line points to God's throne, thus showing the fixity of the earth with respect to the third heaven. That God's third heaven is fixed, we shall have to take at his word, for only God the creator can supply the reference. The plumbline, in turn, holds the *plummet,* a lead ball. In Isaiah 28:17[3] this plumbline over Jerusalem connects Jesus (verses 9-13) with the righteous on earth. In Amos 7:7[4] the LORD shows Amos the plumbline of Isaiah 28 and prophesies that the promised tribulational desolation (verse 9) "will not again pass by them any more." The "wall" of verse 7 upon which stands the LORD must be the temple wall showing the cosmological heavenly alignment of the place where God puts his name. Zechariah calls attention to this plumbline when prophesying the rebuilding of the temple (Zechariah 4:10). He associates the plummet with the cosmic events of Revelation 1 through the seven candles, "...for they shall rejoice, and shall see the plummet in the hand of Zerubbabel with those seven; they are the eyes of the LORD, which run to and fro through the whole earth."

The plumbline shows that salvation comes down, as in Psalm 19, to the earth; note the symbolism of the plummet, being made of lead which is considered the basest of metals, residing closest to the earth, representing man who cannot save himself (Ephesians 2:8-9). The plumbline points from earth to heaven (Jesus being the plumbline and our way to heaven,) and it also points from heaven to earth, bringing judgment upon Jerusalem, as we see in 2 Kings 21:13.[5] Note that the word "line" in 2 Kings 21:13, Psalm 19, and many other places is a geocentric notion in that it is the geocentric, diurnally-rotating heavens that produce the lines.

The Effects Delineated

Yet there are other moral degeneracy effects involving heliocentrism. Take the occult practice of astrology, for example. Heliocentrists believe that the sun, moon, and planets all affect the earth in one way or another. Most particularly, it is held that the gravity of the sun, moon, and planets to varying degrees perturbs the earth and its creatures. A geocentric worldview will not permit the gravity of other celestial bodies to directly affect the earth. Thus it is that geocentricity provides even less "scientific" grounds for astrology than does heliocentrism; for if gravity is allowed to affect the earth, then one could postulate all sorts of subtle, hitherto unsuspected effects of the astral bodies upon the human soul. Indeed, astrologers do exactly that. In geocentricity, the only physical effect that heavenly bodies can have upon the earth and its inhabitants are influx (that is, shooting stars, incident radiation, cosmic rays, etc.) plus those effects due to the knowledge of their existence.

As further support for the link between heliocentrism and astrology, let it be noted that in the several Mideast locations where mosaic floors of the zodiac have been found, every one of them pictures the sun (in the form of Apollo riding a flaming chariot) and not the earth at the center of the zodiac. Thus they place the sun at the very center of the starry sky. All these factors point to a link between heliocentrism and astrology.

Conclusion

In summary, what disturbed the Reformers about heliocentrism and why they tried to combat it was that they recognized however dimly, that moral relativism and superstition would have a more favorable climate to grow in a heliocentric culture than in a geocentric one. The Reformers foresaw that heliocentrism would weaken man's perception of the Bible as the authoritative Word of God.

It turneth itself...

— Job 38:14, *Young's Literal Translation*

9

ALLEGED HELIOCENTRIC VERSES

Over the last 400 years several Bible passages have been presented as promoting heliocentrism. This is done exclusively by heliocentric Christians in their zeal to make the Bible more palatable for the atheist and agnostic who seem to have so little difficulty in accepting the obvious geocentricity of the Bible.

Despite the insistence of these heliocentrists, no passage has gained wide (let alone universal) acceptance. There is not even agreement among heliocentrists as to which references support heliocentrism. The entire foundation for heliocentrism is modern "science." This is not the case for geocentricity where there is not only scientific support but also scriptural support. Since there is no universal agreement among heliocentrists on one single heliocentric verse in scripture, can we conclude anything else but that the proposed verses are primarily due to flights of fancy on the part of their advocates?

A passage once held to promote heliocentrism, though now largely abandoned, is Job 38:14.[1] This verse is embedded in a moderately complex tapestry of pronouns so that the surrounding verses, twelve through fifteen, should be quoted in order to ascertain the meaning of the fourteenth verse:

[12] Hast thou commanded the morning since thy days; and caused the dayspring to know his place;

¹³ That it might take hold of the ends of the earth, that the wicked might be shaken out of it?
¹⁴ It is turned as clay to the seal: and they stand as a garment.
¹⁵ And from the wicked their light is withholden, and the high arm shall be broken.

A few heliocentrists point to the phrase "It is turned" and conclude that this refers to the turning of the earth. Let's look at that more closely.

That the dayspring is a type of Christ we know from Luke 1:78 and 79 where Zacharias praises God for the Christ child, whose coming he refers to with the words:

⁷⁸ ... whereby the dayspring from on high hath visited us,
⁷⁹ To give light to them that sit in darkness and in the shadow of death, to guide our feet into the way of peace.

Notice the wording. Both the visitation by the dayspring as well as the commanding of the morning have inherent in them the notion that it is the dayspring which moves. Thus the twelfth verse is actually a geocentric reference embedded in the supposedly heliocentric verse. The dayspring knew his place, not only here on earth but also at the right hand of the Father.

An analysis of the pronouns reveals that it is indeed the earth that is turned as clay to the seal and that the "they" of the fourteenth verse refers to both the morning and the dayspring. When it comes to the word "turned" in "it is turned as clay to the seal," the heliocentric apologist refers to some ancient signet rings that have been found. Now a signet ring is used to seal and in this case, the rings presumably sealed clay tablets. The heliocentrist maintains, without support of any kind, that the tablet was rotated under the ring and that it is that rotational motion which is referred to in the fourteenth verse. Actually, there seems to be no proof that either ring or tablet were ever rotated to form a seal, it would be too easy to counterfeit as the pattern would be a mess; never be the same.

So the analogy is circumstantial at best, supported only by a private interpretation of the word "turn" in verse fourteen.

It is no secret that in English the word "turn" need not always mean, "rotate." We say that milk *turns* sour, for example but milk does not start to spin as it "turns" sour, nor does it spin faster and faster as it gets more and more sour. So it need surprise no one that the Hebrew word used here, *haphak,* is rarely if ever used in any overt sense of turning. *Haphak* is generally used in the sense of *turning* from one's prior lifestyle or the *turning* of the hand in order to help someone. Its most active form is found in Judges 7:13 where *haphak* is used to describe a cake of barley tumbling into the Midianite camp. The other Reformation translations are no help to the heliocentrists here either since their corresponding languages lack the ambiguity of the English word "turn." Diodati, in the Italian, reads "*mutti in diverse forme*" which literally means "mutated into diverse form." The Dutch *Statenbijbel* reads "*verandert*" which is roughly equivalent to the English word "changed" and literally means, "to be othered." Thus all the Reformation translations are totally consistent with the English Authorized Bible and they are totally at odds with the interpretation of the heliocentrists.

Other objections, too, could be raised against a heliocentric interpretation of Job 38:14. First, there is the presence of the conditional, "might," which appears twice in the thirteenth verse and which, coupled with the fact that the reference is to the judgment, means that the dayspring is not presently shaking the wicked out of the earth and that thus the earth is not now being "turned as clay to the seal." Secondly, the use of the expression "is turned as clay to the seal" indicates a constant expenditure of energy in order to keep the turning going. This is contrary to Newton's first law of motion which states that a moving (or turning) body will keep moving (or turning) as long as there are no forces imposed upon it. Newton's laws, of course, are the very cornerstone of the heliocentrists' "proofs" for the alleged motions of the earth. If the verse is heliocentric in nature then it would appear to violate Newton's first law. This is what Young has done in the chapter quote where he maintains that the earth "turneth itself." To be heliocentric and still be scientifically correct, the verse should read "it is turning as clay to the seal." Thirdly, all Reformation translators had the word "rotate" at their disposal, yet none were led to use it in connection with this verse; not even the Holy Ghost himself in the Hebrew.

What, then, is the true meaning of the verse? There is an obvious meaning which could not be expressed more clearly than in the present wording. As a seal is pressed on clay or wax, the clay moves to fill in the grooves built into the seal. In so doing, the clay wells up in a convection-like motion, a turning motion, and fills in the seal's grooves. This interpretation is entirely consistent with the Bible. Although most modern versions read "changed" instead of "turned," the motion of the clay under a seal is more accurately defined as "turning" since the clay remains clay and does not "change" into anything else. Such a turning motion of the earth could be responsible for uncovering the graves of the wicked at the last resurrection which is consistent with the context of the verse. A "change" will not uncover the graves and thus is not at all consistent with the context.

Even in this present world there is abundant evidence of such a type of "turning" on the part of the earth. There are rock beds which have been folded and bent as if they were pushed aside by tremendous weight. These are especially prevalent in mountain regions where some of the more severely disturbed are commonly referred to by geologists as having been "overturned." Such phenomena could also have occurred at the continental split of Peleg's day.

Conclusion

The heliocentrists' attempts to promote Job 38:14 and other passages as indicative of the rotation and motion of the earth makes God out to be either a clumsy grammarian or a poor scientist, ignorant of Newton's first law of motion. No alleged heliocentric verse has withstood the test of time.

Thy will be done in earth as it is in heaven.

— Matthew 6:10

10

ORDINANCES OF HEAVEN

Job 38:33 introduces what most heliocentrists consider to be the bastion of heliocentrism in the Bible; the ordinances of heaven:

> Knowest thou the ordinances of heaven? canst thou set the dominion thereof in the earth?

Heliocentrists believe that the bands of Orion and the sweet influences of Pleiades mentioned in Job 38:31 refer to gravitation. When the Bible mentions "ordinances of heaven," again the heliocentrists immediately read "the laws of gravity." In other words, heliocentrists believe that the biblical references to the ordinances of heaven refer to the principles of physics as those principles are taught in the twentieth century.

It is not at all difficult to show that such cannot be the interpretation of Job 38:33. Note especially that God asked Job if he, Job, could "set up the dominion" of the ordinances of heaven in the earth. This phraseology implies that the ordinances of heaven are not currently in effect in the earth. Now since gravity is presently effective in the earth, gravity cannot be considered as one of the "ordinances of heaven" to which God is referring as he addresses Job. After all, if the ordinances of heaven are already in effect here below, then instead, should God not have said, "hast thou set the dominion thereof in the earth?"

One may object that this line of reasoning is weak, but there are other indications in scripture that imply that the ordinances of heaven referred to in Job 38 do not have dominion in the earth today. Take our chapter quote, Matthew 6:10 for example:

Thy kingdom come. Thy will be done in earth, as it is in heaven.

Why pray for God's will to be done in earth if it is already being done? And are the ordinances of heaven not part of God's will, especially when they are used to symbolize the permanence of God's covenant in Jeremiah 33:20, 21, 25 and 26? These verses read:

[20] Thus saith the LORD; If ye can break my covenant of the day, and my covenant of the night, and that there should not be day and night in their season;
[21] Then may also my covenant be broken with David my servant, that he should not have a son to reign upon his throne; and with the Levites the priests, my ministers. . . .
[25] Thus saith the LORD: If my covenant be not with day and night, and if I have not appointed the ordinances of heaven and earth;
[26] Then will I cast away the seed of Jacob, and David my servant, so that I will not take any of his seed to be rulers over the seed of Abraham, Isaac and Jacob: for I will cause their captivity to return, and have no mercy on them.

Note that in Jeremiah 33:25 the Lord draws a distinction between the ordinances of heaven and the ordinances of earth, as if to say that these two sets of ordinances are not the same. This supports the conclusion we drew earlier from Job 38:33.

Such a distinction between the things of earth and the things of heaven is also drawn in 1 Corinthians 15:40-41 where Paul wrote:

[40] There are also celestial bodies, and bodies terrestrial: but the glory of the celestial is one, and the glory of the terrestrial is another.

[41] There is one glory of the sun, and another glory of the moon, and another glory of the stars: for one star differeth from another star in glory.

To claim that these verses merely refer to the different brightness of the sun, moon, and stars is to ignore both the context of 1 Corinthians 15:40-41 as well as the fact that the celestial bodies are contrasted with terrestrial ones; the contrast is not celestial with celestial.

All of the aforementioned verses point to a difference between things celestial and things terrestrial. These differences are also inherent in the ordinances of heaven and the ordinances of earth. Thus the ordinances of heaven cannot be restricted or equated to what is popularly called the "laws of physics." Actually, the so-called "laws of physics" are not "laws" at all; for if they were then God would break the "law" every time that he performed a miracle. Take the "second law of thermodynamics," for example. One of the implications of the "second law" is that the dead cannot be resurrected; nevertheless, Jesus resurrected Lazarus and others and thus violated the "second law." When Jesus ascended into heaven, he violated both the law of gravity and Newton's second law, which states that for every action there must be an equal and opposite reaction. When God spoke the universe into existence, he violated the first law of thermodynamics which states that energy (or matter) can neither be created nor destroyed. Thus the "laws" of physics are "laws" only in the traditions of men. They are not God's inviolable laws or ordinances.

Some of the ordinances of heaven and earth are explicitly stated in the Bible. Among the ordinances of earth is Genesis 8:22:

While the earth remaineth, seedtime and harvest, and cold and heat, and summer and winter, and day and night shall not cease.

It has been argued that because of this verse Joshua's long day could only have been an optical illusion at best.[1] The argument is that if Joshua's long day and Hezekiah's sign are not optical illusions local to Israel, then day and night shall have ceased and so God would have violated his promise to Noah, that is, the promise of Genesis 8:22. But read the verse carefully. It says that day and night shall not cease; it does not say that they shall all be of exactly the same duration. Nor does the scripture say that they cannot pause. A day does not "cease" simply if it is lengthened.

Finally, it is written in Daniel 2:21 that God:

> . . . changeth the times and the seasons . . .

If Joshua's long day violates God's promise to Noah, then does this verse also contradict the promise to Noah? Of course not. Clearly, then, there is no inconsistency between the "ordinances of heaven" as mentioned in the Bible and the doctrine of geocentricity as also clearly taught in scripture. Nor for that matter do variations in the length of the day nor in the length of seasons contradict Genesis 8:22. After all, day and night, as periods of light and darkness, are each six months long at the earth's poles, but only about 12 hours long at the equator.

Jeremiah 31:35-36 specifies some of the ordinances of heaven, particularly those of the sun, moon, and stars:

> [35] Thus saith the LORD, which giveth the sun for a light by day, and the ordinances of the moon and of the stars for a light by night, which divideth the sea when the waves thereof roar; The LORD of hosts is his name:
> [36] If those ordinances depart from before me, saith the LORD, then the seed of Israel also shall cease from being a nation before me for ever.

Here the ordinances include how light is produced and for what purpose. Nothing is said about any ordinances involving motions or lack of motions on the part of celestial bodies.

The ordinances of the sun, moon, and stars were specified at the time of their creation in Genesis 1:14-15, where we read:

[14] ...to divide the day from the night; and let them be for signs and for seasons, and for days, and years:
[15] And let them be for lights in the firmament of heaven to give light upon the earth...

Genesis 1:16 adds that the sun is to rule the day and that the moon and stars are to be co-regents over the night. These, then, are the ordinances of heaven which are referred to in Jeremiah 33 and Job 38.

In connection with the ordinance that the sun is to rule the day while the moon and stars are to rule the night, physics Professor Harold Armstrong made a very pertinent observation. In a letter to the author dated 19 March, 1977, Professor Armstrong writes:

Genesis 1:16 says that the greater light, which everybody, I think, grants to be the Sun, was to rule the day. The Hebrew word is the ordinary one to state that e.g. a king rules over a country; ... But what, in this context, is the day? According to 1:5 it is the light. In other words, it is day wherever it is daylight; and that applies to interplanetary space. Even out beyond Pluto it is daylight; the light from the Sun there is still much stronger than full moonlight here on Earth.

How, then, does the Sun rule this territory? To rule a territory could mean to control what happens in it. The Sun, then, controls what happens in interplanetary space, *viz.*: the motions of the planets. It controls also the motions of the irregular or occasional objects there, *viz.*: comets and meteoroids, and nowadays an occasional rocket. In other words, the motions of these things are ordered to the Sun, and (although it is now hindsight) that could have been de-duced from Scripture. So their motion, with respect to the Sun, could well be the same as it is by the heliocentric the-ory (which can be called Newtonian, not Copernican or Keplerian); consequently nothing about those motions can serve as evidence against the [geocentric] Tychonic theory.

However, these arguments could not give Scriptural support to a completely heliocentric theory. For the lesser light, which, I think, almost everyone takes to be the Moon, was to rule the night. Now according to the heliocentric theory, and the interpretation adopted, the Sun would be ruling both day and night; for in controlling the motion of the Earth it would be controlling the motion of the dark side as well as that of the light one. But the Tychonian theory does not encounter any such difficulty.

The point that Professor Armstrong is making is this: the night is that cone of darkness, the shadow of the earth, which is ruled by the moon; the moon occasionally even enters the shadow but is never completely darkened by it. Such an event is popularly called an "eclipse of the moon." Any place where the sun's light would fall would be part of the day; any place the sun's light would not fall is part of the night. Consider the night to be only the cone of darkness which is the earth's shadow. Then in the heliocentric system the shadow, along with the earth, orbits the sun and so is controlled or "ruled" by the sun. The scripture would then be wrong in insisting that the moon and not the sun rules the night (Figure 5).

Conclusion

In summary, we noted that the Bible isolates the following ordinances of heaven: first, that the sun is a light for the day; second, that the moon and stars are for lights at night; third, the ordinances include the means by which said light is produced; fourth, the celestial bodies are for signs; fifth, they are also to be for seasons and that the seasons as well as day and night (as periods of light followed by darkness) shall not cease until the end of the earth shall come. As was noted in the chapter on Joshua's long day, said day is a type of a long day which is yet to come. As such it and Hezekiah's sign are signs to Israel. Thus the two events (Joshua's

Long Day and Hezekiah's Sign) both conform to the "ordinances of heaven" since one of those ordinances is that the sun, moon and stars are to be for signs; but regularity of planetary and satellite motion or rotation is definitely not a biblically-supported ordinance of heaven. These are the ordinances of heaven which the Bible identifies for us. God's question to Job would appear to indicate that there are others of which we are presently ignorant. Yet here, too, we found not a shred of evidence for heliocentrism.

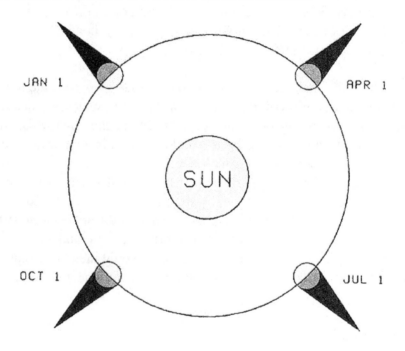

Figure 5a: *The sun rules the night*

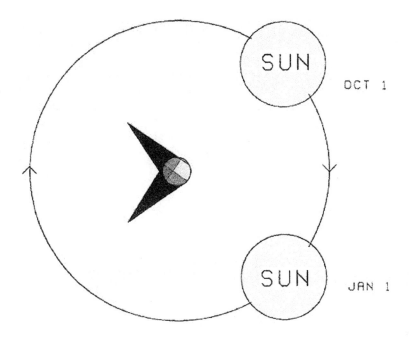

Figure 5b: *The sun does not rule the night*

In the heliocentric system the night, along with the earth, orbits the sun. This violates the Bible's principle of the separation of the powers of darkness and light. On the other hand, in the geocentric system the night orbits the earth with a period of one day and the separation of powers is maintained.

In the first place inanimate nature is, after all, part of the world, so that any philosophy of the world claiming to be truly comprehensive must take notice of the laws of inanimate nature; and in the long run such a philosophy becomes untenable if it conflicts with inanimate nature. I need not here refer to the considerable number of religious dogmas to which physical science has dealt a fatal blow.

— Max Planck[1]

11

GEOCENTRIC MODELS

Heretofore we have looked at the theological issues of the Copernican Revolution, but in the realm of science we have confined ourselves to a criticism of heliocentrism without presenting more than a promise of geocentricity. We have examined scientific observations which, when taken at face value, proclaim the universe to be geocentric. We have also noted that absolute proof of either heliocentrism or geocentricity is lacking unless one accepts the testimony of the Bible as such an absolute proof. Since the time of Copernicus and Kepler, modern science has geared itself to decoding the universe; so we cannot expect it to accept the Bible as any sort of authority whatsoever, let alone to acknowledge the Bible's God. Thus we must deal with the issue of whether or not there are any valid geocentric models.

Ptolemaic Model

Historically, the first geocentric model is the one commonly known as the Ptolemaic model (Figure 6). It is usually represented as the quintessential geocentric model, and much is made of its demise at the hands of Galileo Galilei. Even astronomers and historians who should know better claim that Galileo's discovery that

Venus exhibits moon-like phases disproved the Ptolemaic model. All that Galileo's observations actually meant insofar as the Ptolemaic model was concerned, was that the radii of the epicycles (Figure 7) were much larger than had previously been suspected; and all that Kepler's elliptical orbits meant to the Ptolemaic model was that two of the epicycles could be combined into one ellipse (Figure 7). But by the time of Galileo, the Ptolemaic model had for too long been associated with a category of Greek models which embodied the philosophy of *geocentrism*. Geocentrism is the belief that the universe was made up of impenetrable, concentric spheres (Figure 8). Galileo's observations of the phases of Venus and the satellites of Jupiter (as well as the spots on the sun, for that matter) were fatal to geocentrism; but they need not have been fatal to the Ptolemaic model *per sé,* and they have nothing against geocentricity.

Advanced Potential Models

Modern geocentric models start in 1898 with a paper by the German physicist, Paul Gerber.[2] Gerber was able to show that if the universe rotates around the earth once per day, that then the usual so-called proofs of heliocentrism (the bulge of the earth's equator, the stationary satellite, the Foucault pendulum, etc.) would be present just as we see them. Gerber's model was crude by comparison with modern geocentric models partially because his was a pioneering work and partially because in order to prove his point, he assumed an advanced gravitational potential. The latter assumption basically reverses cause and effect. For example, the usual explanation for earthquakes is that they are due to stress build-up along cracks in the earth. When the stress reaches the breaking point, the earthquake happens and the spin of the earth is affected. In an advanced potential, the earthquakes are due to stresses and strains within the rotating universe which causes a corresponding strain build-up in the earth. Once the universe's strain snaps, the earth slips and the earthquake happens (usually along a weak point like a fault), and the universe adjusts its rotation rate accordingly.

Figure 6: *The Ptolemaic System*

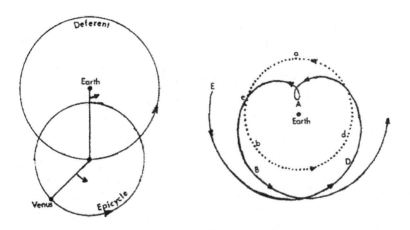

Figure 7: *Epicycles*

Left: The Ptolemaic system modeled the motions of the planets by the use of epicycles which are circles whose centers lie on the circumference of another circle. The *deferent* and *epicycle* of Venus are shown. Right: When the two circular motions are combined, the cycloid (solid line) is obtained. The dotted line shows the sun's path about the earth and capital and lower-case letters respectively show the relative positions of Venus and the sun in their orbits. Note: in the Ptolemaic system the earth was not truly at the center of the deferent but was slightly offset. Ptolemy did not know the distances to the planets, had he known them the path of the sun about the earth would be the deferent with the sun at the epicycle's center and the epicycle's radius equal to the distance between the sun and the planet.

If the reader finds an advanced potential too mystical or unsatisfying, consider another example. Mathematical solutions of field emissions (for example, the mathematics describing the emission of radio waves) require that a signal come in from infinity before the same signal can be transmitted out into space. In other words, when a radio transmitter sends out radio waves, the waves can be mathematically described by trigonometric sines and co-sines; but such a wave traveling through space cannot just start in the middle: that would be like an ocean wave suddenly forming as a sheer vertical cliff of water – it just doesn't happen. For the math to work in the radio transmitter example, there must be a cor-responding radio wave coming in from infinity to generate the sig-nal. This *advanced signal*, as the signal coming in from infinity is called, is generally dismissed as unphysical, being merely a math-ematical artifact. An advanced potential works much the same way. Effectively it acts as if the universe anticipates the position of a planet or anticipates changes in any and every body in the uni-verse.

In the case of the earthquake, the advance potential can be said to "cause" the earthquake. In that case the earthquake registers the earth's response to the advanced potential. That response changes the shape of the earth, and that change in shape is transmitted back to the universe. In turn, the universe shifts its rotation rate, starting at the surface of the earth and radiating out into space at the speed of light. That is the idea behind Gerber's advanced potential. One sees theological overtones of God's control versus the universe's here, and such are not necessarily far-fetched. However, such questions are beyond the scope of this book.

Thirring's Models

Gerber's model is interesting because there may be something to an advanced potential, especially since it is indistinguishable from the usually-assumed retarded potential; but Gerber's model is also limited. With the advent of the special and general theories of relativity in 1905 and 1916, a new emphasis was placed on Mach's principle and the principle of equivalence. In 1918 the German physicist Hans Thirring[3] wrote a paper in which he examined the behavior of bodies inside a rotating shell. His model tried to solve the puzzle of what happens if the universe were a rotating shell: how would pendulums, satellites, winds, and so forth behave near the earth?

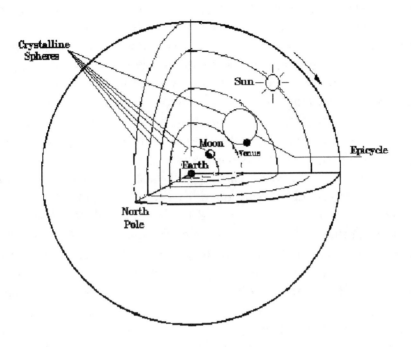

Figure 8: *Crystalline spheres*

The crystalline sphere version of the Ptolemaic universe had the planets confined to rolling along transparent glass spheres. To account for epicycles, smaller spheres rolling between the spheres were invoked (see "Venus").

Thirring discovered that they would behave pretty much as we see them behave, although not exactly. The mismatch he took to be due to incompleteness of his model. Nevertheless, what Hans Thirring discovered was that the gravitational field inside the shell was not zero, as expected in Newton's gravitational model, but that there arose certain forces inside the shell away from the center. These forces are analogous to the centrifugal and Coriolis forces. Now here is a telling distinction: in classical, heliocentric, relativistic physics, the centrifugal and Coriolis forces are technically not forces at all but are termed "fictitious forces" or "effects"; but what Thirring demonstrated was that in a geocentric system, these are no longer "fictitious forces" but real forces. Even more specifically, in a geocentric framework the centrifugal and Coriolis forces are identifiable as *gravitational forces*. This means that the so-called proofs for the rotation of the earth, the Foucault pendulum, the earth's equatorial bulge, the stationary satellite, and so on are not proofs at all, being equally explained by Thirring's geocentric analysis. In fact, since the geocentric model encompasses the entire universe and has no fictitious forces, one could say that the alleged proofs for heliocentrism actually prove geocentricity instead.

Later that same year, Thirring published a second paper with Lense.[4] Lense and Thirring obtained pretty much the same result as Thirring had achieved in his earlier paper, but they did so using a different model: instead of assuming the universe to be a rotating sphere, they modeled it as a rotating disk. Lense and Thirring further discovered that the rotation of a body should have a gravitational effect on other bodies. For example, when the Voyager spacecraft flew by the planet Jupiter it followed a certain path. If the satellites of Jupiter were to rotate more slowly or more swiftly, or if the length of Jupiter's day were to change, Voyager would have followed a slightly different path. This effect, called the *Lense-Thirring effect,* is not yet detectable; but physicists hope to improve their measuring capabilities enough in the next couple of decades to be able to detect it and to see if Lense and Thirring's analysis is correct. The papers by Lense and Thirring set the stage for another look at the so-called proofs of the rotation and orbital motions of the earth; for those "proofs" started looking less and less sure.

Thirring's is not the only geocentric analysis nor is it the best. In 1952 Møller published a text on relativity in which he arrives at the same conclusion as Thirring but by assuming the universe to be a ring instead of a shell. His model is akin to looking at the effect that would be due to the Milky Way, or the average effect of the solar system rotating about the earth; whereas Thirring's is more representative of the effect the universe has as a whole).[5] This section was omitted in Møller's second edition (1972) for certain metaphysical reasons, not because of an incorrect initial analysis: we shall say more on those metaphysical reasons later.

Other Geocentric Models

There have been other mathematical expositions showing that the physics of the geocentric universe is the same as the heliocentric. Birkhoff[6] has taken an approach in which he combined the Coriolis and centrifugal forces to be part and parcel of the definition of gravity. G. Burniston Brown[7] arrived at geocentric solutions from Newtonian gravity and used a purely classical approach. Moon and Spencer[8] took a classically-oriented look at Mach's principle and arrived at a geocentric model. Nightingale[9] has also derived a non-relativistic geocentric model. Rosser[10] expanded on the Lense and Thirring papers explaining how the outer reaches of the universe could not only be moving many, many times the speed of light, but also how the universe would not fall apart, even if it were rotating trillions of times per second. All of these physicists (and there is not a geocentric Christian in the bunch) conclude that there is no detectable, experimental difference between having the earth spin diurnally on an axis as well as orbiting the sun once a year or having the universe rotate about the earth once a day and possessing a wobble centered on the sun which carries the planets and stars about the earth once a year. In none of these models would the universe fly apart, nor would a stationary satellite fall to earth. In every one of these models the astronauts on the moon would still see all sides of the earth in the course of 24 hours, the Foucault pendulum would still swing exactly the same way as we see it in museums, and the earth's equator would still bulge. In other words, each of these effects is due to either the centrifugal force, Coriolis force or some combination of the two and can be totally explained in any geocentric model.

Barbour and Bertotti's Model

The best mathematical, as opposed to geometric such as Tycho's geocentric model (p. 117), to date is that of Barbour and

Bertotti.[11]   Barbour and Bertotti's model is extremely fruitful,
though incomplete.   Starting with the fact that energy can neither
be created or destroyed, they formulate that statement in a particular way called a *Hamiltonian*.   From that Hamiltonian, Barbour
and Bertotti develop a set of equations describing motion in general
throughout the universe.   Eventually they derive Kepler's and
Newton's laws, the perihelion precession of Mercury, a "critical
velocity" which is the speed of light, and electrostatic effects.   They
also derive certain relativistic effects without ever invoking
relativity.   They discover that the laws of physics for the universe
as a whole are different than those for small systems; the former
they call *protophysics,* the latter is called *local physics*.   Barbour
and Bertotti further find that by assuming the universe to be rotating — by assuming that it cannot matter to physics and geometry
whether the earth rotates or the universe rotates — that then a lot of
different and heretofore unrelated physics falls into place into a co-
herent whole.   In other words, their geocentric model is more general and potentially more fruitful than the current heliocentric
(acentric) model.   In short, the geocentric model reflects reality better than does the heliocentric model.

Barbour and Bertotti's physics is not complete, but it can be
made complete with more effort.   Lest one be tempted to fault them
for a not-yet-complete model, remember that the Copernican model
has a three-hundred-year head start of intensive mathematical development.   Barbour and Bertotti's approach promises to be able to
integrate much if not all of physics into a single theoretical framework.   That is the philosophy inherent in geocentricity.

So it is that we find that time after time, in respected physics
journals, papers have been published which show that the geocentric and heliocentric models are equally valid.   Theoretical physicists know that this has to be the case because otherwise, the laws
of physics would depend on one's location in the universe.   If
heliocentrism can be proven, then the laws of physics should be
different on the moon than in an airliner, and different again on the
surface of the earth.   We are reminded that the only way one could
ever prove heliocentrism or geocentricity is to go outside the
universe and to take a look around out there.

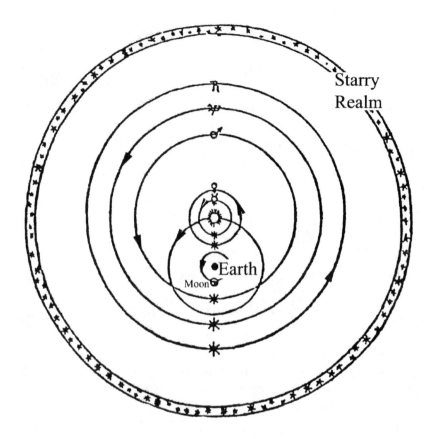

Figure 9: *The Modified Tychonic Model*

The model explains all observed phenomena. The sun is at the center of the circle representing the starry realm or the firmament. The shell it stylized, being actually billions of light years thick in the model. Irregularities in the distribution of stars in the firmament causes a one-year vibration of the entire universe so that the sun follows the circle running through it and centered on the earth. The planets orbit the sun, and the sun sees the earth as if it orbited it. We are looking at this model from the third heaven. If we were in the model there is no way we could tell the difference between this model and the model we were all taught in school.

12

THE FIRMAMENT MODEL

In previous chapters we have referred to phenomena designed to test for or demonstrate both earth's revolution around the sun and rotation. While experiments designed to test for the rotation of earth do show such relative rotation, experiments designed to detect the orbital motion directly do not. Both sets of experiments were designed to reveal the motion of the earth relative to a light-bearing medium called the æther. Yet in the twentieth century, relativity, the theory proposed to explain the lack of evidence for the motion of the earth through the æther, has reportedly done away with the æther. In recent years, however, the concept of the æther is coming back in vogue, albeit in a different form. We shall examine that next.

The Plenum

Historically there have been two versions of the æther. The older of the two views the æther as a *plenum* — an infinitely dense medium. In the nineteenth century, the theory of the *luminiferous æther* was developed. That æther is an extremely rarefied, vacuous one which was thought to carry light waves in much the same way as air carries sound waves and water carries water waves. Presently the evidence is stacked against the luminiferous æther, although in a sense one could view gravitational and other fields as rare æthers. In any case, doing so still does not match the concepts of the luminiferous æther envisioned in the last century. For example, the Michelson-Morley experiment could be explained if the medium bearing the light was dragged by the earth around the sun. If that is so, however, then the æther should also be dragged along with the earth's rotation, which it evidently is not. The luminiferous æther is not nearly as fruitful to physics as is the plenum æther.

The notion that the æther is an infinitely dense medium was first proposed by Greek philosophers. Eventually they concluded that if the medium in which we are thus embedded were infinitely dense, that then there would be no such thing as motion. Their argument was that one could not move if one were encased in lead, and lead isn't even infinitely dense. However, a careful analysis reveals that the plenum model is not so easily dismissed. God, for example, is omnipotent, infinite, and omnipresent. One cannot cut a region of space so small that God's power therein is not infinite. Hence God is a plenum. Yet, as Acts 17:28 records: "in him we live, and move, and have our being." The proper analogy is not one of being encased in lead: instead, a more fitting analogy is found in the air around us. There are fifteen pounds of air pressing on each square inch of our bodies, yet we are not crushed by this weight because there is an equal pressure inside our bodies which negates the crushing weight of the atmosphere. Similarly, the restriction against motion in a plenum is only against straight-line (rectilinear) motion, but cyclical or wave-like motion makes the plenum æther a viable model again.

So in a plenum motion in a perfectly straight line is not allowed; but circular, elliptical, rotational, or undulatory motions are allowed. Furthermore, as if to underscore the point, straight-line motion has never been observed anywhere in the universe — no, not by any experiment ever conducted by man. It is this fairly recent discovery that a plenum, as long as it is eternal and uncreated, will allow closed-path motion, that has given University of Cambridge professor Harold Aspden the impetus to re-examine the æther as a plenum.[1] With his plenum-æther model, Aspden is able to explain a number of phenomena, such as ball lightning, which have thus far eluded explanation by physics. It is Aspden's view that rotation of parts of the æther gives those rotating parts the properties of mass, gravitation, and electromagnetism. His model easily derives some of the "relativistic" effects which otherwise take very complicated mathematical contortions to obtain; and Aspden does so from purely classical considerations. Aspden's model of the æther is not at all radical or new. He perceives the æther in a classical sense: that certain electromagnetic phenomena result from taking the *curl* (a mathematical operation) of the æther. But his view of the æther as a plenum is rather innovative and his is the first fruitful plenum-based æther model in several centuries.

A plenum-æther solves many of the objections which were raised against the rare-æthers over the last century-and-a-half. Because of the Greek dismissal of the plenum, scientists envisioned the æther as a rare, thin medium, much like air but even thinner. That kind of æther must obey the rules of very small numbers. A plenum, by contrast, follows the rules of infinite numbers. For example, any portion of the plenum, no matter how small, must be infinite. In particular, this means that there is an infinite amount of plenum-æther inside the earth. Furthermore, any arbitrarily-sized volume of the æther must contain the same amount of plenum-æther as any other arbitrary volume, namely, an infinite amount. Hence, there is as much plenum-æther inside the earth as there is in the rest of the universe. As such, it is meaningless to imagine the relative masses of earth and cosmos to *necessarily* be significant in terms of their relative motions. That this is so can be seen by the successes of the geocentric models presented in the previous chapter.

But the plenum-æther cannot fully account for all that is observed. Nor is it entirely consistent with the Bible. We must modify Aspden's æther to bring it in line with both physical and scriptural evidence. We shall not be concerned here with any mathematical derivations.[2]

Ex Nihilo

We start at the beginning with absolute nothing. The tendency is to treat "nothing" as a "thing," but its name, "no-thing" belies that. "Nothing" cannot have any properties or attributes. In particular, "nothing" cannot have length, volume, time, or intelligence. It can have neither beginning nor end. It cannot have an origin, and it cannot be a thing. In short, it cannot have the property of existence and so cannot exist. Since it is true that "absolute nothing" cannot exist anywhere at any time, then its inverse must also be true that "absolute everything" must exist always and everywhere. Now do not confuse *absolute everything* with absolute*ly* everything. This absolute existence must have all the inverse properties of nothingness. Whereas the nothing has no size, its inverse must be infinite in extent or omnipresent. Whereas nothing has no knowledge, its inverse must be omniscient. Whereas nothing has no existence, its inverse must have infinite existence. Whereas nothing has no power, its inverse is omnipotent. These are precisely the characteristics of God as presented in the scripture. (Note that these characteristics require God to have a character or personality also.) Thus we have arrived at the necessity for the existence of God as inferred from the very existence and order built into the universe. This observation also illuminates the error of the big-bang hypothesis, namely, that the big-bang-produced universe is too small and too uncharacteristic to be realistic.

So there was nothing at all before God, and God came from nowhere because there is nowhere God could come from. Hence God is reasonable and he even invites us to reason with him, for he says: "Come now, let us reason together" in Isaiah 1:18. For God to truly be omnipresent and omniscient he must be a plenum in the fullest sense of that word; but God is more than the material plenum of the Greek philosophers and Aspden. God is intelligent, creative, and all-powerful. As is taught in Romans 1:20a:

For the invisible things of him from the creation of the
world are clearly seen, being understood by the things that
are made, [even] his eternal power and Godhead.

It is God's eternal power and Godhead that undergirds the creation
and that provided the "stuff" of which the creation is made.

Given a plenum æther, how can the universe be finite and created? In looking at nature, we do not see that it exists with the
properties of a plenum; that is, the properties of God, although pan-
theists claim the contrary. The key to this puzzle lies in understanding how a created, finite æther can be made to look indistinguishable from an uncreated infinite æther insofar as material objects (protons, electrons, neutrinos, photons, etcetera) are concerned. The key to that understanding is to be found in the firmament of Genesis chapter 1.[3]

The Firmament

At the start of the second day of creation the earth was still
formless and void in the deep; but during the second day God removed the deep from off the surface of the earth. He did this by
creating the firmament, which God called "Heaven."

Much has been written on the firmament, most of it pure
speculation. It has been suggested that the firmament was a metal
shell surrounding the universe. Others have suggested that it was a
canopy of water, or water vapor, or water ice surrounding the earth.
The problem with the latter interpretation is that the sun, moon,
and stars are placed *inside* the firmament on the fourth day;
whereas, the canopy model requires them to be on the *outside*. A
discussion of whether or not there ever was a canopy is beyond the
scope of this book. Here our position is that evidence for a canopy
cannot be adduced from Genesis 1.

Of the above two models for the firmament, the former seems
most consistent with the scripture; but is it really? If the stars are
created inside the shell surrounding the universe, then one could
most definitely say that they are inside the firmament. After all, we

say that there is air *inside* a balloon, don't we? This is no different. The problem arises when we discover that "God called the firmament Heaven." If the shell model is correct, then the Scripture should have said: "God called the interior of the firmament Heaven." Yet all agree that the heaven mentioned here relates to "outer space" as opposed to the atmosphere mentioned in the first verse of Genesis. Can it be that the firmament is the vacuum of space? Then why would God imply it to be "firm?"

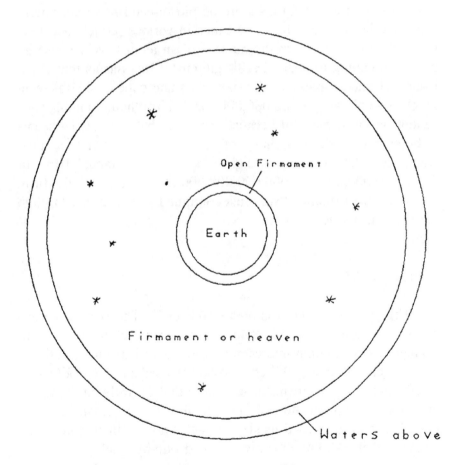

Figure 10: *The firmament according to the Bible*

In order to see the firmness of space, we must look very closely at it. The question is ultimately one of whether or not space has a fabric, a substance. We all know that in looking through a microscope we see smaller and smaller things until eventually we see molecules which consist of atoms. Individual atoms have been seen in microscopes, but beyond that, we must use a mathematical microscope. Through the theoretical microscope, we "see" that the atom consists of electrons, protons, and neutrons. The neutron is made up of an electron plus a proton plus a neutrino. Other particles have been "seen" for short times in various particle accelerators. Now the density in the nucleus of an atom is very dense indeed, amounting to about 2×10^{14} gm/cm^3. This means that a collection of nuclear particles the size of a sugar cube (one cubic centimeter) would weigh 200,000,000 tons! Firm though that is, such cannot be the firmament because the space between nuclei seems to be empty. Indeed, a chunk of the universe the size of a sugar cube, on the average, weighs in at only about 10^{-29} or 0.000,000,000,000,000,000,000,000,000,001 ounce: hardly firm. So to find the firmament we must continue looking further through our theoretical microscope.

Planck Particles

The size of the atom is about 10^{-13} cm.[4] The size of the nucleus is about a thousandth of that. As we proceed to smaller and smaller scales, nothing interesting seems to be happening until we get to a scale of about 10^{-33} cm. At that size called a *Planck length,* fascinating things happen; for it is there that we truly hit the fabric of space. To appreciate just how small a Planck length is, let us note that if we increased its size to that of a man, then man would be the size of 100,000,000 universes laid side-by-side!

At a scale of the order of 10^{-33} centimeters, we find that the warp and woof of heaven comes into focus. Physics attempts to derive relationships between the different properties of objects. Such relationships typically involve certain constants: values which are generally assumed not to change over time. The speed of light is such a constant. So is the gravitational constant. It turns out that there are relationships among these constants themselves, and those relationships all express themselves to specifics at the Planck length. For example, the Planck length itself, L^*, relates Planck's constant (a unit of angular momentum or spin-energy), h+, the speed of light c, and the gravitational constant G to give a length of 1.616×10^{-33} cm. By the same token, the constants give us a fundamental unit of mass M^*, called the *Planck Mass,* which is 2.177×10^{-5} gm. The corresponding basic unit of time, the Planck time, t^*, is 5.391×10^{-44} sec. Lastly, the fundamental unit of temperature T^* can be derived by introducing Boltzman's constant, k, and it gives a temperature for the firmament of 1.417×10^{32} K; a most fervent heat not observed anywhere in the universe.

Modern science is not certain as to the meaning of these numbers, but the most popular explanation at present is that they signify particles which pop into existence, exist for about 10^{-44} second, and then pop out of existence again. These particles, called *Planck particles,* form the basis for various cosmological theories such as strings, superstrings, 10-dimensional space, and so on.

One of the interesting properties of a Planck particle is that it has the same size as both its deBroglie wavelength and its black-hole (Schwartschild) radius for its mass. For most of the twentieth century it has been known that particles do not move in straight lines. Instead, particles such as protons and electrons move in waves. Those waves, called *deBroglie waves,* vary inversely with mass, that is, the lighter the particle the longer its wavelength. Hence an electron is "larger" than a proton, although the latter is much more massive. This is attested to by the observation that the electron "orbits" or "surrounds" the proton when the two are combined in the form an atom. The deBroglie wavelength for a particle of mass M^* is L^*. As for the black-hole radius, if matter is squeezed into a smaller and smaller volume, eventually its gravitational field is so packed that light cannot escape from it; hence the term "black hole," as one cannot see it. The size to which a mass M^* has to be compacted before becoming a black hole is L^*.

Properties of the Firmament

So it seems that we are engulfed in a sea of Planck particles. The particles can be viewed as constituting a pervasive medium which acts like an ideal fluid (meaning that there is no friction). The density, R, of that fluid is an astounding 3.6×10^{93} gm/cm^3. To appreciate how dense that is, let us return to our sugar cube model. Recall that if the sugar cube was filled with nuclear matter, that then it would weigh 200,000,000 tons. Let us try to envision such a cube made up of Planck particles. The numbers are incomprehensible. For example, the mass of the entire universe is estimated to be about 2×10^{54} gm. Packing everything in the universe into the cube would only give us a density of 2×10^{54} gm/cm^3, far short of the Planck medium's 3.6×10^{93} gm/cm^3. That means that one would have to pack 2×10^{39}, (that is: 2,000,000,000,000,000,000,000,000,000,000,000,000,000) universes into the cube to arrive at the appropriate density! If this doesn't qualify for the name of "firmament," then what does?

A medium of such a high density as the firmament has some interesting properties. One would think, for example, that it would be impossible to move in such a medium, just as one could not move if encased in iron — even if one were made of solid iron! Normally this is true, but the deBroglie wavelengths of nuclear particles are so long compared to that of the Planck particles that firmament is transparent to them. This is similar to why light can travel through a "dense" medium such as glass instead of being stopped cold on impact. So we have our first prediction of the firmament model: motion through the firmament will be effortless as long as we are not dealing with nuclear particles approaching a mass of M^* or, more particularly, energies of $M^* c^2$. The firmament will not allow elementary particles to approach that energy without absorbing them. Has such been observed? Not yet; for physics labs have not come anywhere near creating particles that massive.

Should they ever succeed, however, we can expect the particle to disappear in t^* seconds.

In order to hide its finite properties from the material in the universe, the firmament, as this created medium is called, could not be allowed to reveal its true age, or density, nor allow the determination of absolute positions within it. In this way, time and position would be kept *indeterminate*. The indeterminacy of position and time (or energy and momentum) is popularly called the *Heisenberg Uncertainty Principle*. The truth of this principle has been demonstrated by numerous experiments. In short, this means that the firmament is an underlying medium. The atoms and galaxies of our universe are merely tiny, insignificant disturbances in the firmament. Because of the Heisenberg Uncertainty Principle, matter is totally unaware of the firmament's existence. If it were not for scripture, we would be equally unaware of it. Only on extremely small scales, distances of the order of a Planck length, does the firmament show through the warp and woof of space.

Now the question arises whether or not the firmament is stable. In particular, such stability is called *mechanical equilibrium*. A body is in mechanical equilibrium when its energy is evenly distributed between the rotational and gravitational energies. Ozernoy[5] has derived the equation for mechanical equilibrium of rotating bodies. For the firmament there is a natural frequency of 10^{47} cycles per second (Hz). Normally one would expect this to be the rotational speed, but the radius of the firmament does not appear in the expression for its angular velocity, so the value could also be interpreted as a simple frequency, such as the rotational frequency of the Planck particle. (The number is not exact, but its dependence on the size of the universe allows for great uncertainty.)

The Firmament Found

The firmament which God created on the second day is an extremely massive structure. Its properties are manifold and in a very literal sense, it determines the very physics of the universe. It was either superimposed on already created atoms, or else the atoms were created throughout it as it was formed. Geocentrists are currently searching for a dependence on the properties of the firmament and its daily rotation. With the waters removed to above the firmament, the light now was suspended in the firmament which carried it about the earth once a day. The firmament itself dictates the frame of reference for the light and all the particles in the universe. The speed of light was thus, and still is, defined with respect to the firmament.

From the perspective of modern science, the firmament as put forth in Genesis chapter one is a very viable scientific option. It is a super-dense, created medium which mimics a plenum. It does so both by keeping absolute position and time indeterminate within it (Heisenberg Uncertainty Principle), as well as allowing only wave motions and disallowing absolutely straight-line motion. The firmament reacts instantly to any changes within it (in about 10^{-44} sec). Material objects can only become vaguely aware of its existence on extremely large scales (of the order of the size of the universe) and on extremely small scales (of the order of sub-nuclear particles). None of these phenomena are new, all have been noted before in the scientific literature.

We know that the difference between a heliocentric theory and a geocentric theory is one of relative motion only, and that such a difference has no physical significance.

— Sir Fred Hoyle[1]

13

THE GEOCENTRIC VIEW

Sir Fred Hoyle, the author of the chapter quote, was one of the world's foremost and outspoken cosmologists. If anyone should know whether or not science has proven heliocentrism, it would be someone of Hoyle's stature. Yet, as is evident by the quote, Hoyle disclaims any such proof. Bouw has collected numerous statements from physicists, all of whom concur with Hoyle.[2] Unfortunately, it is sometimes in the "best interest" of a science not to present the whole truth in introductory texts, and the alleged proofs of heliocentrism constitute one such case. The only time a student might hear differently is in advanced courses such as those on relativity, and even there, it may be "hidden between the lines." In general, the higher the degree a man has earned in physics and astronomy, the more likely he will recognize the truth of Hoyle's statement.

So it is that there are many people who, having had one or two courses in physics or astronomy, scream bloody murder about the geocentric ignoramuses who want to throw science back into the Dark Ages. Characteristic of those people is a perverted view of authority: they deem science a greater authority than the clear wording of the Bible. "After all," they claim, "if the geocentrists are correct, then according to the Bible, trees have hands." They fail to see that every normal person since Adam has had no difficulty recognizing the figurativeness of the verse; whereas from Adam until Copernicus, no one knew or had any inkling that the

Bible's geocentric verses were not to be taken literally. After all, if the truths of the Bible are timeless, then we can't have new, external revelations overruling old ones. Particularly, this means that some new scientific "revelation" called "evolution" cannot overrule the plain sense of the word "day" in Genesis 1: neither can the scientific "revelation" of heliocentrism overrule the plain sense of the passages presented in earlier chapters. Because of this, and the aforementioned deception of introductory physics, astronomy, and science texts, we must address some particulars which, although already covered in the broad scope of the material presented heretofore, must be dealt with in greater detail. First, though, we need to clear up some common misconceptions.

Common Misconceptions

It is generally believed, without evidence, that in the geocentric model the sun, moon, planets, and distant stars all *orbit* the earth once per day. There is no orbiting involved. What is happening is that the firmament is rotating. Now the nature of the firmament is such that it defines all the physics of the universe, both the local and the universal, protophysics (Chapter 11, page 116). This means that all the "laws" of physics are part and parcel of the firmament and that the firmament acts like a medium for the laws of science. So it is that in a geocentric model the sun, moon, and stars do not gravitationally orbit the earth daily any more than that a molecule in a top gravitationally orbits the center of the top. In the case of the spinning top it is the fibers and material of the top which carry the molecules around the axis of the top. By the same token, in the geocentric model it is the fabric of the firmament which carries the universe about it.

A second common misconception is related to the first and that is that the geocentric universe requires that the sun orbit the earth once per year. Again, this is not the case. In a geocentric universe Newton's (or Einstein's) laws must be fulfilled just as in a heliocentric universe. Newton's law of gravity states that from the sun's perspective, the earth must be seen to revolve about it once per year. It matters not to the sun whether the earth actually does so or appears to do so; remember that we are talking about relative motion, not absolute. If the firmament were to possess a wobble (about which we will say later) which carries the sun, planets, and stars about the earth once a year in such a way that the earth seems to describe an orbit around the sun, then the sun and the universe are content that the law of gravity is being satisfied. Remember, the physics of the universe which specify the law of gravity is fastened to the firmament, not the earth or sun.

A third misconception is that the speed of light cannot be exceeded. This argument means that if the stars and planets are further away than Saturn, they would be moving faster than the speed of light in their daily motion about the earth. There are two problems with this statement. First, the daily motion is one of rotation, and relativity (which dictates that the speed of light is a speed limit) is said not to apply to rotation. This is claimed because relativity cannot account for the Sagnac effect, an effect which violates relativity's postulate that the speed of light cannot be exceeded. More practically, though, relativists maintain that in a spinning universe the gravitational field increases as one goes further and further from the axis of rotation. Relativity allows that it is the gravitational field which dictates the speed of light in any part of the universe. Thus the further one goes from earth, the faster the speed of light in a rotating universe. But the true resolution is this: the laws of physics, including any laws about a speed limit, are defined relative to the firmament.

It is not the case that the universe is rotating once per day inside the firmament. On the contrary, the firmament does the rotating and the bodies of the universe seldom go much faster relative to the firmament than a few hundreds to a few thousands of miles per second, far, far below the speed of light. Hence, if the speed of light (3×10^{10} cm/sec or 186,272 miles per second) is a speed limit in the universe, it is so only relative to the firmament. Because of its tremendous mass and density compared to the material universe, it is a small thing for the firmament to rotate once a day. For rotation, there is no problem with violating the speed of light, even at the most remote edge of the universe.

The last misconception we shall look at now is the one which claims that the laws of physics should be different in a geocentric universe than in a heliocentric universe. Time and time again this has been shown to be false. What this misconception claims is that phenomena such as the Foucault pendulum, the stationary satellite, the flight of ballistic missiles, indeed, the very equations on which the space program is based must be different in a geocentric universe. This is the very misconception which Ernst Mach tried to counter in the late nineteenth and early twentieth centuries.

To understand this, think of it this way. Imagine a non-rotating coordinate system fastened to the center of a spinning globe in the middle of a room. Imagine that somewhere in the room there is a basketball player standing, dribbling a ball. Initially, even though the globe is spinning, the coordinate system is not spinning and we describe the motion of the ball mathematically in terms of the coordinate system attached to the globe. Now imagine that the coordinate system starts spinning with the globe. It should be intuitively obvious that the behavior of the basketball and player is not affected by whether or not the coordinate system is spinning. In other words, just because some imaginary coordinate system is spinning, one cannot claim that the ball should bounce back up, away from the player's hand. This is the case claimed by Mach and the geocentrists. Geometry is an imaginary concept and cannot be allowed to dictate the physics as a function of the coordinate system.

Yet there are those who insist that a geocentric universe must give a different physics. Unwittingly they argue that the behavior of the basketball is different in a spinning coordinate system than in a non-spinning one. Those subject to this misconception have assumed that the coordinate system, the geometry, is the ultimate reality instead of a language used to describe reality. This is the ultimate reality of Plato, but is wrong and borders on idolatry.

Figure 11: *Geocentric explanation of the seasons*

The sun traces out the indicated path in the course of the year. Each adjacent layer in the helix represents one day. The sun's position is at its lowest point, on the first day of winter. The sun spirals upward, one rotation per day, until it reaches its northernmost point, marked by the X. It then starts a down-ward spiral, again crossing the equator and back to its southernmost point where it started from. Each spiral is actually about ten days, so the figure shows a year of 36 days. North is up, so it is clear that the sun shines most on the northern hemisphere in summer (at the X) and most on the southern hemisphere in winter ("Sun"). The figure below shows only the first day of summer (top), the first days of spring and fall (center), and the first day of winter (bottom). (The earth's size is greatly enlarged.)

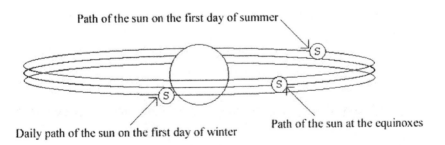

Path of the sun on the first day of summer

Daily path of the sun on the first day of winter

Path of the sun at the equinoxes

Daily versus Yearly Motion

There are two primary motions which we will consider in this chapter. Additionally, we could account for the motion about the center of the Milky Way, the motion relative to the center of the Virgo cluster of galaxies, and numerous other motions. Ultimately, all we need to consider is the motion of the earth relative to the universe. We have seen elsewhere that any attempt by a body or force to move or twist the earth will be resisted by the universe and that the latter will restore the earth to its central position. Such forces include those of the moon, artificial satellites, earthquakes, and so forth. The mechanism behind this is that the behavior of the firmament is indistinguishable from a plenum. The universe is so light compared to the firmament that its effect on the firmament amounts to less than the effect a single electron has on the entire universe! Then, too, the firmament defines the laws of physics. This means that it is no violation of the laws of physics that the firmament spins about the earth once per day, that it has a wobble of a year, plus one of about 28,000 years, plus whatever motion may be necessary to specify the laws of physics. One could view this relationship between the firmament, the earth, and the universe as if the fact that the earth is located at the center of the universe means that there are certain "cracks" in the firmament, which "cracks" (which are technically called *coupling constants* in physics) specify at least the local physics if not the protophysics. The daily rotation is easy to picture, but it is harder to see the yearly motion. We shall look at some of the yearly effects next.

The Yearly Motion

An oft-asked question is how the seasons are described in a geocentric framework. Much the same as in the heliocentric model. The key to understanding the geocentric approach is to understand that in the course of a year we reckon 365 days (366 if a leap year). During that time the stars are seen to rotate about the earth 366 times (367 if a leap year). In addition, the sun travels in a north-south pattern in the course of a year, resulting in a spiral motion when viewed from the earth or the outside of the universe (Figure 11). On the first day of summer (called the *summer solstice*), the sun is as far north as it is going to go; and on the first day of winter (*winter solstice*), the sun reaches its southernmost point. The first days of spring and fall mark the times that the sun crosses the equator. Geocentricity allows the sun that north-south motion as it is carried by the firmament in a north-south motion due to either irregularities in how the matter is distributed throughout the universe or else to forces imposed from outside the universe. Figure 11b shows the seasons from a geocentric perspective.

Figure 9, pg. 117, illustrates the wobble in the universe which describes the yearly motion of the sun, planets, and stars about the earth. It is important to the understanding of the model that one realize that the yearly motion is not a rotation but a to-and-fro motion which describes an elliptical path the size and shape of the earth-sun "orbit," the circle about the earth on which the sun is located, see Fig. 9. All the planets and stars participate in that motion, including the laws of physics because the motion is an inherent property of the firmament. The result is that parallax, aberration, the annual Doppler shift, precession of the equinoxes, and perihelion precession are all accounted for by the model.

The View from the Moon

One proof of heliocentrism which is becoming increasingly popular is the claim that astronauts, looking from the moon, have seen the earth rotate. This claim is subject to a very subtle error. Imagine our astronauts sitting on a horse on a carousel. As they go round and round on the carousel, they look toward the center where the engine and supports are bolted to the ground. To them, however, the engine seems to be turning on its axis while they stand still. Now, according to the heliocentrists who argue this way, the engine has been proven to rotate and the platform of the carousel has been proven to stand still because the astronauts, from their carousel horses, saw all sides of the central engine as it turned.

Likewise, the astronauts see a rotating earth because the platform they are on is rotating in the opposite direction.

Retrograde Motion

As seen above, one of the most complicated phenomena in geocentric geometry is the annual motion of the sun around the earth. Much of the confusion about annual phenomena stems from an erroneous or incomplete picture of what is involved in the geocentric geometry: and it is merely a matter of geometric perspective. In this and the next two sections we shall look at how the annual motion of the sun around the earth can account for a phenomenon called *retrograde motion.*

The outer planets, which are all planets except for Mercury and Venus, normally move from west to east against their starry backdrop; but at certain times, they exhibit a phenomenon known as *retrograde motion.* At those times, they reverse their motion and travel east to west for some time before resuming their normal eastward travel. The original explanations for the effect were geocentric. Ptolemy introduced the idea of epicycles to explain the phenomenon; so it is not as if retrograde motion is impossible to explain in a geocentric framework. But before we delve into the geocentric explanation, let us present the heliocentric explanation.

Heliocentric View

The heliocentric explanation of retrograde motion is depicted in Figure 12. In that figure, let us assume that the earth is traveling along the inner orbit and that the outer orbit is that of Mars. Since the earth travels faster in its orbit than does Mars, the earth overtakes Mars. As the earth passes Mars, Mars seems to be going backwards among the stars (points 3, 4, and 5 against the background). The explanation is simple enough.

Nevertheless, many insist that the geocentric model will not explain the retrograde motions of the outer planets. Figure 13 shows that such is not the case.

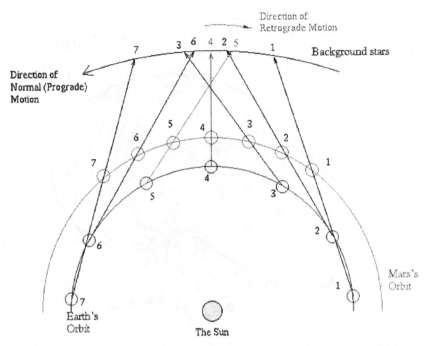

Figure 12: *Heliocentric view of the retrograde motion of Mars*

The Geocentric View

In order to understand the retrograde motion of the exterior planets from a geocentric perspective, we need to understand that in a geocentric model, the yearly motion of the sun around the earth is not made by a turning or rotation of the universe. The motion is due to a cycloidal motion, somewhat like a vibration. The reader can see this by turning to the figure of the modified Tychonic model (page 117) and then sliding the sun, planets and stars along the circle on which the sun is located while keeping the book right-side up. Doing so gives us Figure 13. You'll notice that the motion of Mars along the starry background is the same as in the heliocentric explanation.

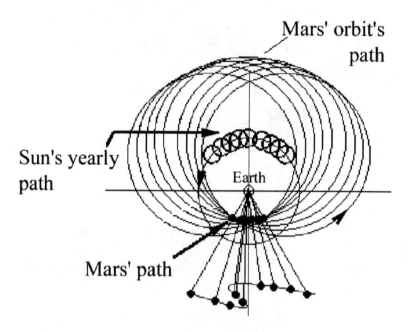

Figure 13: *Composite geocentric retrograde motion diagram*: The earth is at the "cross-hairs" in this diagram. The sun's nine positions are shown along the upper part of the earth-centered circle. Mars' nine positions are pointed to by "Mars' Path." The large slinky-like structure centered on the sun is the nine positions of Mars's orbit as it accompanies the sun in its yearly circuit about the earth.

Illustrative Geocentric Models

Several models have been devised by members of the Association for Biblical Astronomy (formerly the Tychonian Society) to illustrate the behavior of a geocentric universe and its equivalence to the heliocentric model. The first such model was published by Richard Elmendorf and was called the *Celestial Motion Illustrator*. The Celestial Motion Illustrator was simple to construct and illustrated a lot, serving to illustrate both geocentric and heliocentric models. More recently, Elmendorf has constructed a geocentric version of an orrery (a mechanical model of the solar system), but because all his supports are underneath the stars and planets, Elmendorf's model is limited in its motion. A third model was proposed by Bouw in 1984. A 1992 refinement guarantees that his model does not suffer from the same limitation (Figure 14).

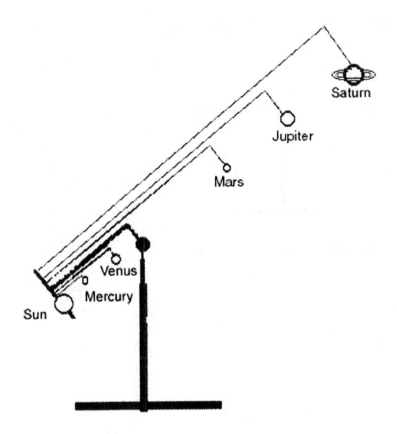

Figure 14: *A geocentric orrery on the first day of winter*

The daily rotation can be added by turning the vertical shaft on which the earth (black ball) is perched clockwise as seen from above. The following figures show the seasons. The planetary motions are ignored, so that the planets effectively follow the same path as do the distant stars.

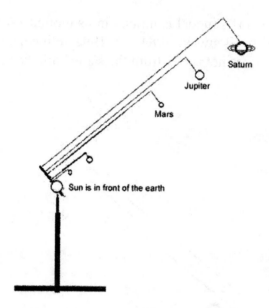

The first day of fall: the sun is crossing the equator northward.

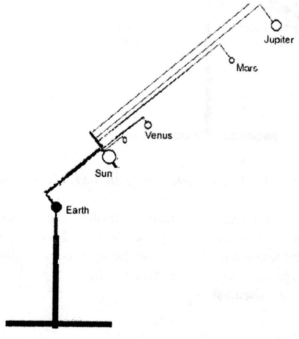

The first day of summer: note that the sun shines on the North Pole

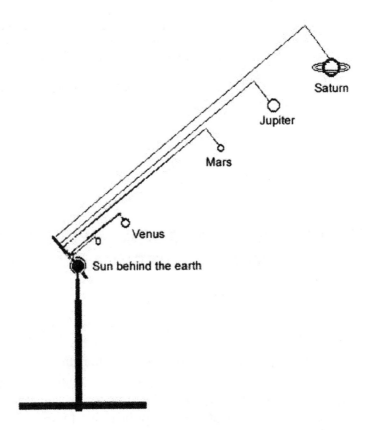

The first day of autumn. The sun is behind the earth descending across the equator. Note that the planets keep the same orientation throughout the year, just as do the stars.

Let us hear the conclusion of the whole matter:
Fear God, and keep his commandments: for this
is the whole duty of man.

—Solomon, Ecclesiastes 12:13

14

CONCLUSION: THE MORAL EFFECTS OF HELIOCENTRISM

In the chapter quote, Solomon truly summarizes the conclusion of our study. We have examined criticisms of the Bible which have been mindlessly applied since the Reformation and found them wanting. The Bible does not use phenomenological or vulgar speech in describing the motions of the sun, moon, and stars. We noted that to question the truth of the application of the word "rise" to the sun in scripture is to cast the same shadow of doubt on the word "rise" when it is applied to the resurrection of our Lord Jesus Christ from the dead. Because of the Copernican Revolution, there has been a steady devaluation of mankind and man's place in the universe and of Scripture in the minds of men.

The Birth of Higher Criticism

The unabridged edition of *Geocentricity* traces the pagan foundations of modern philosophy, and heliocentrism in particular, from its early Pythagorean inceptions through the pagan-classical reasoning of Copernicus and his early followers. In the early seventeenth century, the concept of *revolution* obtained a different shade of meaning than it had thitherto. The concept of revolution, as then applied to celestial bodies, ended up with a much broader, social meaning, changing not only in meaning, but value and significance as well. It was subsequently applied to the areas of politics and theology. This came about not so much because of the upset of the Ptolemaic world view but because Copernicus had succeeded in making a clearly heretical teaching palatable to not only the Roman Catholic Church, but to Protestantism as well. Copernicus and Galileo had succeeded in discrediting the Bible as an authority in the realm of science. This called into question the authority of the Bible in all other areas, too.

Kepler picked up the Copernican idea and worked on it to the point that philosophers and historians both acknowledge him the father of the modern mechanistic, Godless worldview. It was Kepler who envisioned the creation, man included, as pure machine. As such, life loses all meaning and value. Galileo, though forbidden to promote the ideas of Copernicus, succeeded in flaunting the obvious heresy in the face of the Roman Inquisition.

After the Galileo affair, the Bible was no longer considered authoritative in the realms of science, philosophy, and day-to-day reality. Less than 200 years after surrendering the Bible's authority in the realm of physical science, man surrendered its spiritual authority at the hands of the German school of higher criticism, a way of criticizing the Bible which supposedly is based on natural revelation, that is, upon "scientific" principles. Consequently, the Bible became viewed as merely "containing the word of God," that is, a mixture of God's words and man's words. Once it had been received as the very words of God. Now men claim without fear or thought that the Bible is only inerrant in what it claims about "salvation," but that its scientific and dietary claims are quite errant. Others maintain that the Bible "*is* inerrant only in its *original autographs*" which "original autographs" no longer exist anywhere on earth. They do not realize that it is an error to say "**is** inerrant" about the originals in the first place since the word "is" maintains that they still exist. This latter claim obviously denies both the inerrancy of the currently existing Bible as well as denying the preservation of the Bible.

Of the former critical view we find Galileo who stated that "Scripture teaches men how to go to heaven, not how the heavens go." Protestant and Catholic alike echoed "Amen!" The subsequent dismissal of the Bible as authoritative in the natural realm established two priestly castes: the *interpreter-critic* caste, who either tell Believers what God *meant* to say or who will graciously condescend to teach Believers what the long-lost-and-certainly-never-seen-by-him "originals" say; and the *interpreter-scientist* priestly caste who read from the fabled *Book of Nature* to "correct" the errors in the written word.

So it was that with all sound theology summarily dismissed, science opened itself to every crackpot idea under the sun. The occultist, Swedenborg, regularly had spiritual communication with the inhabitants of the moon, stars, and planets who told him that the solar system originally started out as a collapsing cloud of gas and dust which subsequently split into rings and fell together to form the sun, moons, and planets.[1] Laplace plagiarized Swedenborg's revelation, made some minor modifications, and to this day, under the name *Nebular Hypothesis,* it remains the standard superstition of how the solar system formed, despite that physics has again and again shown it to be an unworkable model.

The Revolutions

The revolution of the sciences spilled over into the political realm. Both the American and French Revolutionary wars stemmed more or less directly from the Copernican Revolution. Great Britain had its revolutions, too, but they had been comparatively bloodless. In frustration certain early nineteenth century parties thirsted for the bloody revolution to come to Britain as it had come to France; a revolution which would make Britain safe for the "free thinking" humanist. "Free thinking," by the way, is a euphemism for foul-mouthed, bigoted, intolerant, narrow-minded, superstitious, name-calling railers who oppress all who feel free to think about and conclude for the existence of God. (See any publication put out by any officially atheistic group.) The nineteenth century British case will serve us well to illustrate the morality of modern science and the rationale behind its beliefs.

In the first half of the nineteenth century, the British monarchy still ruled by the *divine right of kings*, the idea that since God appoints rulers, the king rules in God's stead. This idea, which is not at all scriptural, was defended by William Paley (1743-1805) in his work popularly known by the title *Paley's Natural Theology*. The divine right of kings had sometimes been interpreted to mean that the king could do no wrong and was thus free to exercise any of his whims without having to account to anyone. Paley claimed that the Bible was on his side, even though the word "natural" in the title of his book should have given him away. Paley simply abused certain scripture passages and ignored Romans 13:1 which clearly teaches that the king is ultimately responsible to God. Pointing out this very simple fact should have been enough to discredit the divine right of kings when that right was used as a license for evil.

But the political party which was out of power in early nineteenth century Britain had no use for God and his Bible. Under the auspices of the London Geological Society a young lawyer named Charles Lyell (1797-1875) published a three-volume work entitled *The Principles of Geology*. In an effort to promote his work, Lyell asked a fellow radical, Charles Babbage, for his endorsement of the book. Babbage's response, dated May 3, 1832, has a strange ring to it:

> I think any argument from such a reported radical as myself would only injure the cause, and I therefore willingly leave it in better hands.

What of the cryptic reference to "the cause?" As Grinnell phrased it, Lyell's work was:

> ...in support of political liberalism – although ostensibly it was an objective work in science free from any political implications. In his letter of May 3 to Lyell, Babbage was explaining why he would not write a favorable review of the book. Quite wisely, the Whig scientists, like Babbage,

Lyell, Scrope, Darwin and Mantell, did not want the public
to know that that which was being promoted as objective
truth was little more than thinly disguised political propa-
ganda.[2]

In his book, Lyell proclaimed his *uniformitarian principle*: that
the "present is the key to the past," as being the only true scientific
principle. This principle now undergirds all theories of evolution
even though it is more and more falling into disrepute. Yet for
Lyell it was a way to deny the authority of scripture by attacking
the reality of the Noachic Flood. The flood had up to then been
held as the explanation for the deposition of sediments and fossils;
and to that end, it is still more than adequate today. But in order to
discredit the divine right of kings and so to set the stage for revolution, Lyell determined to undermine the supposed biblical foundation for the divine right of kings by discrediting the Bible.
       Lyell made it possible for the theory of evolution to come out
of its hiding place in sociology into the natural sciences. In 1859
Lyell encouraged Charles Darwin (1809-1882) to write his book on
evolution (which some claim was plagiarized from a manuscript
written by A. R. Wallace and sent to Darwin for review). Darwin
was no stranger to evolution. He had learned it from the writings
of his grandfather, Erasmus Darwin (1731-1802), who was ever
the avowed enemy of God and the Bible. By making man out to be
the end result of countless cosmic accidents occurring over millions
of years, any vestige of purpose or meaning for human life that
might have survived the mechanization of Kepler's universe, was
now gone. After Darwin and Lyell, man was demoted to nothing
more than a machine, and at that a cosmic accident.
       After Darwin's book was published, the superstition of evolu-
tion banned God ever further from man's study for truth. With
God excommunicated from the "natural sciences," Karl Marx was
able to write his book, *The Communist Manifesto*, which quickly
became the chief political instrument in the dehumanization and
mechanization of man in this the twentieth century. In the 1920s
Lenin expressed his indebtedness to Copernicus for making the
world safe for Marxism and Communism.

Applied Evolution

Not long after Darwin and Marx, the German philosopher Nietzsche combined their evolutionary, sociological notions into one concept and concluded that man must be evolving into superman. Nietzsche was anything but a great thinker and he was not nearly as bright as his admirer, Adolf Hitler, who correctly reasoned that there can be no such thing as evolution into a superman but that the evolutionary end-product must be a "super race." What people like Hitler, Stalin, Amin, and Mao TseTung each have done to achieve his idea of a "super race" is history. It is applied evolution, complete with the survival of the fittest.

Murphy, Boltzman and the Second Law

We've all seen copies of Murphy's Law and its corollaries. Usually Murphy's Law is stated as "If anything can go wrong, it will go wrong"; but true to Murphy's Law, the statement was not made by Murphy. Who was Murphy and whence his law?

Edward Aloysius Murphy was a U. S. Air Force Captain working on the rocket sled project back in 1949. One day he noted that a technician was installing accelerometers backward on a rocket sled. As a result, Captain Murphy's law was born as: "If there's more than one way to do a job and one of those ways will end in disaster, then someone will do it that way." Later the rocket sled driver, then Major John Paul Stapp, framed Murphy's Law into its current wording. So you see, Murphy was an optimist!

Now consider the case of Ludwig Boltzman, born 14 February, 1844, who was a famous Austrian physicist. Ludwig was among the staunchest advocates of "Murphy's Law" in the early twentieth century. He believed it so much that he committed suicide because of it at Duino on 5 September 1906.

It seems that as Boltzman pondered the philosophical meaning of the second law of thermodynamics (commonly called "entropy"), he got so depressed by the hopelessness of "it all," that he killed himself. Now don't get the wrong idea; Boltzman was not some poor deluded ignoramus on the matter. It was he who generalized the second law and took it out of the realm of thermodynamics and into the realm of information theory and statistical mechanics. In that sense he is most famous for deriving the current formula for entropy as "$S = k \ln w$."

Anyhow, before his suicide, Boltzman lamented that his work on the second law would neither be appreciated nor believed. He realized that such is actually a consequence of the second law itself. Boltzman's understanding of the second law lead him to the conclusion that man has no hope of saving himself because the second law dooms the universe. Nowadays, "everyone" says Boltzman was wrong, that all physicists believe the second law. But do they? If scientists believe the second law then why, in 1976, did they award the Nobel prize to Ilya Prigogine for his *unsuccessful* efforts to circumvent the second law so as to allow for the theory of evolution?

Unfortunately for Boltzman, although he was correct in concluding that his law would not be believed by scientists, he did not realize the extent to which he, himself, would disbelieve the second law. Think about it: could death create death? Could chaos create chaos? In short, could the second law create the second law? Thus there must be a Creator God if anything is to exist!

How do these stories relate to geocentricity? The simple connection is this: one of the predictions of the second law is that the truth is less likely to believed than is fiction. God is less likely to be believed than the Devil's lies, and the Bible is less likely to be believed than the fantasies of deluded scholars. One more example will serve to make the point.

Relativity and Moral Relativism

Whether advertently or inadvertently, relativity has contributed much to the moral dilemma facing modern man. Einstein and his followers proclaimed that relativity was not and is not a theory about morality: that relativity has noting to do with moral relativism, the ancient idea that an action may be moral in one context but immoral in another; that there are no moral absolutes.[3] The pro-moters of relativity claim that such a connection between moral relativism and relativity is the result of faulty understanding, that relativity does not at all say that all physical knowledge is relative and that Einstein held certain things as absolute in his theory. For example, Einstein claims the speed of light as an absolute speed limit for physical objects. Still others say that there is indeed a connection between moral relativism and relativity. Among these is Dean Turner who writes:

> Without uniform time or cosmic moment, the notion of any universally binding distinction between past, present, and future would be logically and empirically inconceivable. ... And as a consequence, there could be no universally valid ideals for making binding moral distinctions, i.e., that are clearly applicable to *everyone everywhere* at a *given* time. ... In fact, I encounter several students in my classes every year who invoke Einstein's theory to justify their anti-moralism.[4]

This conclusion was indirectly corroborated by no less a per-sonage than the agnostic philosopher, Bertrand Russell:

> The collapse of the notion of one all-embracing time, in which all events throughout the universe can be dated, must in the long run affect our views as to cause and effect, evo-lution, and other matters. For instance, the question whether, on the whole, there is progress in the universe, may depend upon our choices of a measure of time. If we choose one out of a number of equally good clocks, we may find that the universe is progressing as fast as the most op-timistic American thinks it is; if we choose another equally good clock, we may find that the universe is going from bad to worse as fast as the most melancholy Slav could imagine. Thus optimism and pessimism are neither true nor false, but depend upon the choice of clocks.[5]

To these statements one can only conclude that good and bad are relative and that they depend upon one's perspective; and this is precisely what Turner has encountered in his students and, I might add, Turner is not alone in his observation.

So modern man faces the prospect that there is no purpose to life, that morality is actually relative and that what is morally right today may be wrong tomorrow or *vice-versa*. Is there then no absolute? Logically it can be shown that there must be at least one absolute. To see this, consider the statement: "There are no absolutes" and note that it is self-contradictory; for if there are no absolutes then it is **absolutely** true that there are no absolutes and the statement itself becomes an absolute. The usual escape to this is to claim that there are no absolutes except for the fact that there are no absolutes. But this leads to what is called a *self-referral paradox* and leaves one with two absolutes, the absolute fact that there are no absolutes save one, and the statement of that fact. Hence there must be at least one absolute.

With such a logically contradictory philosophy and associated life-styles, is it any wonder that this is the age of despair? Such contradiction means that man is not dealing with reality but only with an imaginary world of his own making. Modern psychiatry calls that "psychotic." The modern philosophy, existentialism, only has questions; it has no answers. The Reformers had an inkling of the consequences of the Copernican Revolution and had warned against it. The warning had gone unheeded, becoming a point of ridicule instead. Now we do not claim that heliocentrism is primarily responsible for man's moral dilemma today, but its acceptance did pave the way for a world view which denigrated absolute moral authority to be subservient to man's limited, fallible mind. Heliocentrism's removal of the Bible as absolute authority paved the way for the acceptance of the political lies of evolution and Marxism into man's worldview. The result gave man a lower view of himself and forced him to frame for himself ill-structured questions which can have no answers. Such is the legacy of modern heliocentric science.

In Summary

Looking at the history of heliocentrism, we found that there never has been a sound, logical reason for assuming heliocentrism over geocentricity. We saw that the early Greek philosophers advocated heliocentrism either on erroneous grounds, incomplete analysis, or for philosophical reasons; and not because the evidence ever dictated such. We saw that the same was true for the advent of heliocentrism during the Renaissance. We traced heliocentrism back to its astrological foundation and discovered that the sun, so central in the worship of the Babylonians, is still central in the world's worship services today where altars, more often than not, contain an image of the sun.

In this condensed book, we did not examine most the alleged proofs of heliocentrism; we note simply that they have fallen away into disrepute as man's knowledge of the physical universe increased. We noted that the best that modern science can say is that heliocentrism can only be proven as long as we assume that there is nothing beyond the universe and we select our coordinate system to be (arbitrarily, I might add) fixed on the "fixed" galaxies (the stars are no longer "fixed" enough). All alleged proofs are usually said to have fallen with the advent of relativity; but we noted early on that the modified Tychonic universe readily absorbs most, if not all of them. Furthermore, heliocentrists have, themselves, freely admitted that geocentricity is as good an explanation for the motions of the cosmos as heliocentrism and furthermore, heliocentrists have also constructed mathematical models showing the equality of geocentricity and heliocentrism as physical models for the kinematics of the universe.

It was noted that certain observations belie the cosmological principle and that both direct and circumstantial evidence points to the centrality or near-centrality of the earth in the universe. We have presented the key to understanding geocentricity to be a more complete definition of the æther than has hitherto been formulated, and we have pointed to some of its mathematical properties and capabilities.

But by far our main conclusion is this, that criticism of the Bible on the grounds of heliocentrism are unfounded. The Bible ever has been, and still remains, inerrant with no evidence against it. Any "errors" in the Bible exist only in manuscripts or versions based on "current" human understanding or have been deliberately altered or forged.

We have cited example after example of cases where the scientific "proofs" of one generation fall by the wayside in the next generation. Truly the scientific theories change almost as much as the fashions. Yesterday's science is tomorrow's superstition. The scientific material the unabridged version of this book will eventually go out of date, even as Wilkins' scientific "proofs" against the Bible—namely that it cannot be believed because it says in Psalm 19 that the sun is hot whereas it's been scientifically "proven" that the sun is nothing but a mirror reflecting the light from the lake of fire—went out of date. Yet the Bible will stand and the general scientific principles will remain. No absolute proof of heliocentrism is possible. An absolute proof of geocentricity as presented here is also impossible.

All in all, the *Book of Nature* has proven to be a most fallible revelation when it comes to absolute truth; yet it consistently bears witness to the truth of the Bible and confounds those who have attempted the formulation of a theology based in whole or in part on natural revelation. Much bloodshed and sorrow, famine and birth defects, disease, infection, suicide and mental anguish have come to pass because man does not heed his Creator's command to love his neighbor as himself; and heliocentrism has proven to be the cornerstone for the philosophies which allow man to do so. These things all serve to illustrate the wisdom of Paul's admonition in Ephesians 4:14; that the believer cleave to the words of God, and that "we henceforth be no more children, tossed to and fro, and carried about with every wind of doctrine, by the sleight of men, and cunning craftiness whereby they lie in wait to deceive."

NOTES AND REFERENCES

CHAPTER 1

1   De Morgan, A. 1872. *A Budget of Paradoxes*, 2nd edition; D. E. Smith, ed., 1915, (Chicago & London: The Open Court Publishing Co.), 1, p. 36.

2   Russell, B. 1935. *Religion and Science*, (London, Oxford, New York: Oxford University Press), p. 11 of the 1970 edition.

3   *Ibid.*, p. 16.

4   *Ibid.*, p. 244.

5   Jacobs, Rabbi L. Jewish Cosmology, in *Ancient Cosmologies*, ed. by C. Blacker and M. Loewe, (London: George Allen & Unwin Ltd.).

6   Anonymous. 1976. The Divine Word in Human Words. *The Other Side*, May-June, p. 45. Quote is from pp. 50 through 51.

7   Kuhn, T. S., 1970. *The Structure of Scientific Revolutions*, 2nd ed., p. 137.

CHAPTER 2

1   ⁶ The words of the LORD are pure words: as silver tried in a furnace of earth, purified seven times.
    ⁷ Thou shalt keep them, O LORD, thou shalt preserve them from this generation for ever.

CHAPTER 4

1   E. W. Maunder, 1908. *The Astronomy of the Bible*, (New York: Mitchell Kennerly), pp. 385 ff.

2   Peterson, I. 1990. "Turning Back Time," *Science News*, 137(6):91.

3   Forke, A. 1925. *The World Conception of the Chinese*, pp. 86-87. Forke confuses this account with Joshua's long day.

4   J. Gill, 1810. *An Exposition of the Old Testament*, (London: Matthews and Leigh), Vol. 2, p. 831. Gill's work was reprinted in 1979 under the title *Gill's Expositor*, (Streamwood, Ill. 60103: Primitive Baptist Press).

5   Lowie, R. H. "Shoshonean Talės," *Journal of American Folklore*, 37:298.

6   Thompson, S. 1929. *Tales of the North American Indians*, pp. 42-43.

7   Olcott, W. T., 1914. *Sun Lore of all Ages*, (NYC: G. P. Putnam's Sons), pp. 131-132.

8   A. Caso, 1937. *The Religion of the Aztecs*, (Mexico City: Popular Library of Mexican Culture, Central News Co.), pp. 15-16.

9   Goetz, D. and S. G. Morley, translators. 1950. *Popul Vuh: The Sacred Book of the Ancient Quiche-Maya* is Volume 29 in *The Civilization of the American Indian Series*. Translated from the Spanish translation of Adrian Recinos. Pp. 151-152.

10   Sitchin, Z. *The Lost Realms*. Book 4 of *The Earth Chronicles*. (New York: Avon Books), p. 151.

11   Frazer, J. G., 1914. *Golden Bough*, (third edition), 1:316.

12   Olcot, 1914. *Op. Cit.*, p. 206.

CHAPTER 5

1   Bouw, G. D. 1987. *Bulletin of the Tychonian Society,* No. 45, pp. 25-28.

2   Deane, Rev. W. J. *Joshua, His Life and Times,* (New York: Fleming H. Revell Co.), p.86.

3   Maunder, E. W., 1908. *The Astronomy of the Bible,* (New York: Mitchell Kennerly), pp. 375 ff.

4   Ramm, B., 1955. *The Christian View of Science and Scripture,* (Grand Rapids: Wm. B. Eerdmans Publ. Co.), pp. 156-161.

5   Collett. 1933. *All About the Bible,* pp. 283-288.

6   Boling, R. G., 1982. "Joshua," in *The Anchor Bible,* (New York: Doubleday and Co., Inc.)

7   *Ibid.,* p. 274 versus p. 284.

8   James, 1917. "Hymn of Deborah," in *Biblical Antiquities of Philo.*

9   Israel, R. Manasseh Ben, 1972. *The Conciliator of R. Manasseh Ben   Israel,* (New York: Hermon Press).   This edition contains both volumes of the mid-seventeenth century work. Volume 2, question 10, pp. 12-18.

10   Wilson, R. D., 1930. "Understanding the Sun Stood Still," in *Classical Evangelical Essays in Old Testament Interpretation,* Walter C. Kaiser, Jr., ed., pp.61-65.

11   *Ibid.,* p. 63.

12   *Ibid.,* p. 64.

13   *Ibid.,* p. 64.

14   Bolling, *Op. cit.*

15   Bouw, *Op. cit.*

16   Faulstich, E. W., 1987. Joshua's Long Day...or Joshua's Miraculous Day?" *Its About Time,* January 1987-Shebat 5987, pp. 2-5.

17   Keil and Delitzsch, 1870. *Commentary on the Old Testament,* (Wm. Eerdman Publ. Co.)

18   Gaussen, 1841. *The Divine Interpretation of the Bible,* pp. 246-251.

19   Velikovsky, I., 1950. *Worlds in Collision,* (New York: Dover Press).

20   Rand, H. B. 1968. *When the Earth Turned Over* (Merrimac Mass. 01860: Destiny Publishers).

21   Hanson, J. N. 1978. *Creation Research Society Quarterly,* **15**(1):55.

22   Virgil. *Æneid,* Book IV, 1, 489. Page 105 of Rofe Humphries, translator, 1951. (NYC: Scribners).

23   Totten, C. A. L., 1891. *Joshua's Long Day and the Dial of Ahaz, A Scientific Vindication and A Midnight Cry,* 3rd Edition, (New Haven: Our Race Publ. Co.) Reprinted in 1968 by Destiny Publishers, Merrimac, Mass.

24   Olden, R. L., 1970. "The Lost Day of Joshua," *Ministry,* (November/December). The publication is put out by the Seventh Day Adventists.

25   The translation that follows came from the Cercle Scientifique et Historique, France and Belgium. It is presumably taken from among Crombette's three volumes of *Verdique Historique de l'Egypte Antique.*

26   Aardema, V., 1975. *Why Mosquitoes Buzz in People's Ears,* (New York: Dial Press).

27   Martin. Sinie. Histor. I. 1. p. 25.

28   Gill, John. 1810. *An Exposition of the Old Testament* (London: Matthews and Leigh), vol. 2, p. 831. Gill's work was reprinted in 1979 under the title *Gill's Expositor,* (Streamwood, Ill. 60103: Primitive Baptist Library).

29   Bouw, *Op. cit.*
30   Hübner, J., 1733. *Kurtze Fragen aus der Politischen Historia.*
31   Olcott, W. T., 1914. *Sun Lore of all Ages,* (NY: G. P. Putnam's Sons).
32   *Ibid.*, p. 212.
33   *Ibid.*, p. 215.
34   *Ibid.*, p. 216.
35   *Ibid.*, p. 217.
36   *Ibid.*, p. 218.
37   Caso, A. 1937. *The Religion of the Aztecs*, (Mexico City: Popular Library of Mexican Culture, Central News Co.), pp. 15-16.
38   Goetz, D. and S. G. Morley, translators, 1972. *Popul Vuh: The Sacred Book of the Quiché Maya,* (Norman, Oklahoma), Part III, Chapters 4-7, pp. 172-190.
39   Bancroft, H. H., 1883. *Native Races of the Pacific States,* (5 volumes), Vol. 3, pp. 58-62.
40   Montesinos, F., 1882. *Memorias Antiguas Historiales de Peru.* The manuscript for that book dates from 1648. A translation of it was done by P. A. Means for the Habluyt Society of London in 1920. Notes from Z. Stichin, *The Lost Realms,* (New York: Avon Books), Ch. 7.
41   Frazer, J. G., 1914. "The Magical Control of the Sun," *Golden Bough,* 3rd ed., 1:316.
42   Olcott, *Op. cit.,* pp. 86, 96, 98, and 206.
43   Hill, H. "How to Find a Missing Day," *How to Live Like a King's Kid*, (Baltimore: Logos), Chapter 13, pp. 65-77.
44   Hill, H. 1984. Private correspondence. Letter dated October 1.
45   Hill, *How to Live Like a King's Kid,* p. 66.
46   1978. "Five Minutes With the Bible and Science," *Bible-Science Newsletter,* 8(5):1-2.
47   Hill, in the 1984 letter.
48   Brosche, P., & J. Sundermann, eds., 1978. *Tidal Friction and the Earth's Rotation,* (New York: Springer-Verlag), p. 12.
49   Lang, Walter, 1991. *Job and Science,* (Richfield, MN), pp. 5-6.
50   Based on computer calculations by the author.
51   Drake, S. 1978. *Galileo at Work - His Scientific Biography,* (Chicago & London: Univ. of Chicago Press), p. 228.

CHAPTER 6

1   Burgess, A. J. 1976. December issue of *Christian Century*, p. 1100.
2   *Ibid.*
3   Bouw, G. D. 1978. *Bulletin of the Tychonian Society,* No. 22, p. 1.

CHAPTER 7

1   Both throughly and thoroughly mean "fully, completely, perfectly." Thoroughly has a sense of "in a way that penetrates, that goes right through. It is thus oriented to coming from the outside in. Throughly is interior. It has a sense of "through the whole thickness" and so works from the inside out to the surface. A key distinction in some passages lies in the fact that "throughly" has also a sense of "from beginning to end,

for the whole length of time." This brings the lifetime of the object into play with throughly which is not the case with thoroughly.

CHAPTER 8

1   Kline, M. 1972. *Mathematical Thought From Ancient to Modern Times*, (New York City: Oxford University Press), p. 246.
2   This section is quoted from: Hanson, J. N. 1991. *Ibid.,* pp.33-35.
3   Judgment also will I lay to the line, and righteousness to the plummet: and the hail shall sweep away the refuge of lies, and the waters shall overflow the hiding place.
4   Amos 7:7-9–Thus he showed me: and, behold, the Lord stood upon a wall made by a plumbline, with a plumbline in his hand.   And the LORD said unto me, Amos, what seest thou?   And I said, A plumbline. Then said the Lord, Behold, I will set a plumbline in the midst of my people Israel: I will not again pass by them any more: And the high places of Isaac shall be desolate, and the sanctuaries of Israel shall be laid waste; and I will rise against the house of Jeroboam with the sword.
5   And I will stretch over Jerusalem the line of Samaria, and the plummet of the house of Ahab: and I will wipe Jerusalem as a man wipeth a dish, wiping it, and turning it upside down.

CHAPTER 9

1   Whitcomb, J. C. and D. B. DeYoung, 1978. *The Moon: Its Creation, Form and Significance,* (Winona Lake: BMH Books). P. 15.
2   *Ibid.,* p. 67.

CHAPTER 10

1   Lang, W. 1978. *Bible-Science Newsletter: Five Minutes with Bible and Science,* Vol. 8, p. 2.

CHAPTER 11

1   Planck, M., 1936. *The Philosophy of Physics*, (London: Geo. Allen & Unwin Ltd.), p. 11.
2   Gerber, Paul. 1898. *Zeitschrift fur mathematik physik,* **43**:93. Gerber's paper has been translated into English and is available from the author.
3   Thirring, H., 1918. *Physikalische Zeitschrift*, **19**:23.
4   Lense, J., and H. Thirring. 1918. *Ibid.,* p. 156.
5   Møller, C., 1952. *The Theory of Relativity*, (Oxford: Clarendon Press), pp. 318-321.
6   Birkhoff, G. D., 1944. *Boletin de la Sociedad Mathematica Mexicana*, **1**:1.
7   Brown, G. B., 1955. *Proc. of the Phys. Soc., B,* **68**:672.
8   Moon, P. & D. E. Spencer, 1959. *Philos. of Sci.*, **26**:125.
9   Nightingale, J. D., 1977. *Am. Jrnl. of Phys.*, **45**:376.
10   Rosser, W. G. V. 1964. *An Introduction to the Theory of Relativity,* (London: Butterworths), p. 460.
11   Barbour & Bertotti, 1977. *Il Nuovo Cimento B*, **38**:1.

CHAPTER 12

1   Aspden, H., 1969. *Physics without Einstein*, and 1972. *Modern Æther Science*, (both from Southampton: Saberton Publications.)
2   The interested reader may want to take a look at Aspden's *Physics Without Einstein* and A. E. Whittaker's *History of the Theories of the Æther and Electricity* (New York: Dover).
3   G. D. Bouw, 1987. "A New Look at the Æether," in *Progress in Space-Time Physics*, J. P. Wesley, ed. (Benjamin Wesley Publishers.: Weiderdammstrasse 24, 7712 Blumberg, West Germany). Pp. 104-108. Also: G. D. Bouw, 1987. *Bulletin of the Tychonian Society*, #43, pp. 11-20. The most rigorous treatment is in G. D. Bouw, 1992, *Proceedings of the 1992 Twin-Cities Creation Conference* (Twin-Cities Creation Science Association: Minneapolis), p. 23.
4   For the remainder of the article, the reader who has no sense of the size of a centimeter should bear in mind that a centimeter is a bit under half an inch. Given the nature of the calculations and the uncertainties in the mass of the universe and its size, in what follows, that reader may read "inch" instead.
5   Ozernoy, L. M., 1967. *Astron. Tsirk.* Nos. 405 and 407.
6   Bouw, G. D., 1987. *Locations cited.*

CHAPTER 13

1   Hoyle, Sir F. 1975. *Astronomy and Cosmology - A Modern Course*, (San Francisco: W. H. Freeman & Co.), p. 416.
2   Bouw, G. D., 1990. *Bulletin of the Tychonian Society*, no. 54, p. 24.

CHAPTER 14

1   Swedenborg, E., 1734. *Principia.*
2   Grinnell, G., 1976. *Kronos*, 1:68. Also see R. Porter, 1977. *The Making of Geology*, (New York: Cambridge Univ. Press) and K. L. Taylor, 1978. *Science*, 199:166.
3   Terletskii, Ya. P., 1968. *Paradoxes in Relativity*, (New York: Plenum Press), p. 9.
4   Turner, D. 1979. In Turner and Hazlett, eds. *The Einstein Myth and the Ives Papers*, (Old Greenwich, Conn.: Devin-Adair Co.). Einstein Myth, p. 17.
5   Russell, B., 1969. *The ABC of Relativity*, third revised edition, ed. by F. Pirani, (New York: Mentor Books), p. 141.

The topic of geocentricity—the belief that the earth is fixed in space near or at the center of the universe—is a poorly-understood, much-maligned theory among Christian Fundamentalists, Evangelicals, Jewish people, and Roman Catholics. But the Pope's recent apology to Galileo serves to illustrate both how fundamental the issue of geocentricity really is as well as its relevance to modern theology; otherwise, why bring up the matter?

This book has been an abridged edition of Dr. Bouw's second book, *Geocentricity*, published in 1994. The current volume examined on a popular level, the significance of the Copernican revolution in the light of biblical and scientific evidence. Along the way, the reader will find a worldwide collection of little-known accounts of Joshua's long day and Hezekiah's sign.

Dr. Bouw has had a long-standing interest in astronomy, so much so that he earned a Bachelor of Science in astrophysics from the University of Rochester, Rochester, New York (1967), and an M.S. (1971) and Ph.D. (1973) in astronomy from Case Institute of Technology (now Case Western Reserve University) in Cleveland, Ohio. His intense interest in cosmology led him to a spiritual birth in 1975. Today he is one of the world's foremost experts in biblical astronomy and geocentricity, having written articles on the Star of Bethlehem, the missing mass of the universe, cosmic isotropy, geocentricity, astrophysical evidence for a young universe, the Pleiades, and the fabric of space and time. Dr. Bouw is also the first astronomer to document evidence that the huge clusters of galaxies rotate. He is the director of the *Biblical Astronomer*, as well as the editor of its quarterly which is the first and still the only creationist magazine devoted to astronomy.

In addition to his interest in astronomy, Dr. Bouw is an ardent defender of the inerrancy and preservation of the Holy Bible. To that end he was written a book entitled *The Book of Bible Problems* which is the first treatise treating the major so-called contradictions in the Bible without recourse to copyist errors. The book is available from the Biblical Astronomer office.

Dr. Bouw teaches computer science as a full Professor of Mathematics and Computer Science at Baldwin-Wallace College in Berea, Ohio. (The College does not necessarily share Dr. Bouw's views of the Bible and science.) In addition to his astronomical and astrophysical degrees, he has also earned an M.C.I.S. degree from Cleveland State University. Dr. Bouw married Elisabeth O'Keefe in 1979 and they have two children.

The Geocentric Bible #3

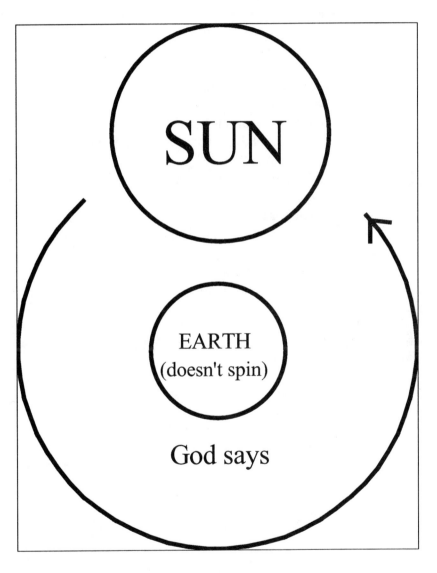

SUN

EARTH
(doesn't spin)

God says

Gordon Bane

Gordon Bane's web page is at www.geocentricbible.com

Interesting web pages:

Geocentricity
www.geocentricity.com
www.fixedearth.com

King James only web pages:
www.kjv1611.org
www.avpublications.com
www.biblebelievers.com/Doege_compare.html

Scientific creationism web pages
www.crs.org
www.icr.org
www.AnswersInGenesis.org

An electric universe is another interesting idea:
www.holoscience.com

DISCLAIMER

Dr. Bouw, the author of *A Geocentricity Primer*, does not necessarily agree with many of the claims made in the *Geocentric Bible*. Most specifically, he disagrees with the small universe model. He does so on the grounds that first, it trivializes sin by minimizing God's spatial separation from it, second, there is no spiritual, scriptural, or scientific reason making a small universe imperative. The advocate of a small universe limits God's power to that which he can conceive by his own understanding, (Luke 18:27).

_____

All Scriptures are from the King James Version
and any deviation from that is unintentional.

FOREWORD

This book has been sent free to:

Christian Churches (Independent)	6,500
Christian Churches (Non-instrumental)	4,512
Baptist Bible Fellowship	2,443
Independent Baptists	1,893
Free Will Baptists	2,448
Lutheran Churches	17,011
Catholic Churches	17,427
Episcopal	7,155
Methodist	29,458
Presbyterian	21,200
Assemblies of God	11,899
Church of God (Cleveland)	3,458
Church of God (Anderson)	1,914
Churches of God	3,145
Mennonite	1,627
Total	132,090

(Additional copies available free)

PREFACE

In 1992 the book *Geocentricity*, by Gerardus D. Bouw, Ph.D., was published by: The Biblical Astronomer, 4527 Wetzel Avenue, Cleveland, Ohio 44109. Web site, www.geocentricity.com.

In August 2000, Dr. Bouw condensed the book to: *A Geocentricity Primer*, a smaller version. This was sent to all 5600 Christian Churches (Independent), Missions and Bible Colleges in our brotherhood. I had a few pages in the back of that book as a Postscript. The second edition included an expanded version of the postscript and was entitled *The Geocentric Bible*. It updated and expanded on those articles in the postscript, but was still based on the two Geocentricity books. This, the third edition, corrects some things in the second edition of *The Geocentric Bible* and expands on it.

There is no scientific proof for or against either heliocentrism or geocentricity. There is no evidence that compels us to believe that the earth is spinning daily, nor orbiting the sun yearly.

Comments and criticism are very much welcome.

> Gordon Bane
> 911 Van Buren
> Hugoton, Kansas 67951
> gbane@pld.com

October 2004

TABLE OF CONTENTS

INTRODUCTION

In 1990, I received literature from the Bible Science Association, which mentioned geocentricity. When I realized what it was talking about; it made me instantly mad and I almost threw it way because I had learned in school that the earth spins on its axis daily, and the sun only <u>appears</u> to revolve around the earth. I kept reading because Bible verses were listed.

This book is based on *A Geocentricity Primer*, which points out the simple mistake in the 16th century of abandoning geocentricity (sun going around a stationary earth) and accepting heliocentrism (earth spinning and going around the sun). There is no proof for or against either theory. All tests, including the stationary satellite, can be explained just as easily from the geocentric viewpoint.

The change in theories damaged our viewpoint of the Bible, which is geocentric. The King James Bible is openly geocentric with many verses like the following: "From the rising of the sun unto the going down of the same" (Psalm 113:3). During creation week, God didn't call the 2nd day of creation "good," as he did every other day. God is telling us it will be difficult to understand the firmament, which we must do in order to understand the Bible.

Since we are dealing with God and not man, we will have many wild statements. Isaiah 55:8 says, "For my thoughts are not your thoughts, neither are your ways my ways, saith the LORD."

Isaiah 34:16, "...none (no verse) shall want her mate...," says every verse is explained or supported and made complete by another verse. Let's let our imagination run wild, if necessary, to stay <u>with</u> God as he leads.

Chapter 1

SCRIPTURES

These are a few of the many scriptures showing that the Bible is geocentric.

ECCLESIASTES 1:4-7

[4] One generation passeth away, and another generation cometh, but the earth abideth for ever.

[5] The sun also ariseth, and the sun goeth down, and hasteth to his place where he arose.

[6] The wind goeth...returneth

[7] All the rivers run...return again.

We are to take things in context. We know the generations, wind, and rivers actually move, so the sun <u>also</u> literally, physically moves being carried daily around the earth by the rotating firmament. The earth <u>absolutely</u> is not rotating.

The Bible is openly geocentric. Genesis 15:12,17 says, "And when the sun was going down" and "when the sun went down." Psalm 104:19 says, "the sun knoweth his going down."

PSALM 50:1

"The mighty God, even the LORD, hath spoken, and called the earth from the rising of the sun unto the going down thereof." The earth and the sun are both mentioned together in this verse and it is the sun that is moving in relationship to a stationary non-spinning earth.

SON AND SUN

Malachi 4:2 says, "But unto you that fear my name shall the Sun of righteousness arise with healing in his wings." If the S<u>un</u> doesn't really move (rise), then the S<u>on</u> hasn't risen. Judges 9:33 says, "...as soon as the sun is up, thou shalt <u>rise</u> early, and set upon the city..." "Rise" means to physically move. Every jot or letter is important (Matt. 5:18). God is saying that the sun revolves daily around the earth.

SWORD OF THE SPIRIT

Rom. 9:17 says, "For the scripture saith unto Pharaoh, Even for this same purpose have I raised thee up, that I might shew my power in thee, and that my name might be declared throughout all the earth." This verse is quoting Ex. 9:16, which God himself personally said, "And in very deed for this cause have I raised thee up, for to shew in thee my power; and that my name may be declared throughout all the earth." This means that "Scripture saith" is synonymous with "God saith." They can be used interchangeably. All the trustworthiness of God Himself rests upon the written Word of scripture. Daniel 10:21 says, "But I will show thee that which is noted in the scripture of truth...." God's written word is the scripture of truth.

John 12:48 says, "...the word that I (Christ) have spoken, the same shall judge him in the last day." Our reward may be damaged by verses that we have bypassed.

GENERATIONS

Genesis 2:4 says, "These are the generations of the heavens and of the earth when they were created, in the day that the Lord God made the earth and the heavens." Webster's Dictionary says "generation" means formation of a geometric figure by motion of another, and also that one geometric figure is a circle. "Generations" here, means moving in a circle.

The earth, if it were spinning, is not daily making a geometric figure. It is stationary, in one place. The verse is talking about motion "in the first day." So, only the heavens (firmament and sun) are making a geometric figure or circle by daily revolving around the earth.

DAMAGE

The world, by promoting as "fact" that the earth spins daily, only wants to embarrass the Bible by then claiming that heliocentrism is true. The unsaved could then do what they want to do with no fear of punishment. The unbelievers, being lost anyway, have no investment in the Bible. If it turns out that they are wrong, the world will not care.

The church has a huge investment in heliocentrism, because it contradicts many verses and takes away authority from God's word. If heliocentrism turns out to be false (and it is nothing more than which ball is going around the other), we could lose part of our reward in heaven.

PERILOUS

The word "perilous" is used only in II Timothy 3:1, which says, "This know also, that in the last days perilous times shall come." Perilous! What could be more perilous in the New Testament than past events in the Old Testament? It must be something that is spiritual rather than physical. Mankind caused perilous times with his denial (without proof) of geocentricity in the 16th century. In the eyes of the world, the Bible now has a scientific error, and has lost its authority!

"Wherefore lay apart all filthiness and superfluity of naughtiness" (James 1:21). Superfluity means oversupply. There is now an oversupply of evil. Either God deceived mankind for the first 5600 years or Satan has deceived everyone for the last 400 years.

Romans 14:1 says, "Him that is weak in the faith receive ye, but not to doubtful disputations." What could be more doubtful than the geocentricity- heliocentrism debate? It has already been changed once with no proof. Obviously, the sun comes up each day whether the sun orbits the earth or the earth spins. "But foolish and unlearned questions avoid" (2 Tim 2:23).

In Gen. 1:1 God created

THIS   NOT THIS

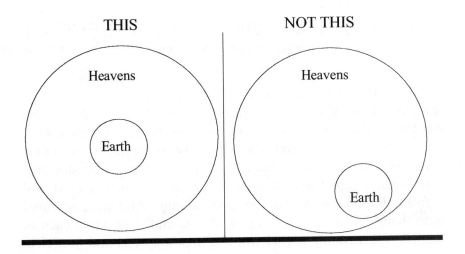

Chapter 2

THE FIRST PART OF THE FIRST SECOND OF CREATION

"If I have told you earthly things, and ye believe not, how shall ye believe, if I tell you of heavenly things?" (John 3:12.) We must understand verses that tell us how God created the universe.

(Acts 2:1,2,3) "And when the day of Pentecost was fully come, they were all with one accord in one place. And suddenly there came a sound from heaven as of a rushing mighty wind, and it filled all the house where they were sitting. And there appeared unto them cloven tongues like as of fire, and it sat upon each of them." The rushing mighty wind, (Christ's power) and fire (electromagnetism), were used when he created the heavens and the earth. He established the physical universe in the same way as he founded the spiritual (the church).

Isaiah 34:16, "...none (no verse) shall want her mate..." Every verse is explained or supported and made complete by another verse. Let's let our imagination run wild, if necessary, to stay <u>with</u> God as he leads.

The "microseconds" information reprinted on page 177 is taken from Robert Gentry's book, *Creations' Tiny Mystery*, p. 27. He is head of Earth Science Associates, Box 12067, Knoxville, TN 37912, and worked in the Oak Ridge National Laboratory. He found physical evidence that God created granite-type rocks in less than one second. A thin slice of rock is put under a microscope, which then shows little rings of discoloration called *radiohaloes*. These come from the decay of uranium and polonium. The rings are formed from the decay of high-energy particles, which impact the rock. They are clearly seen.) Secular scientists find no fault with his lab work; they just disagree with the conclusion – "...he commanded, and it (the earth) stood fast" (Psalm 33:9). This verse has a mate to support it: "He sendeth forth his commandment upon earth: his word runneth very swiftly" (Psalm 147:15).

We learn from astronomer Dr. Gerardus Bouw that, mathematically, the plenum could spin at 10^{44} times per second. It could, perhaps, spin 10^{23} times per second as the electrons do in an atom. The further one goes from the earth, the faster the speed of light in a rotating universe. Unreal? A very large amount of information can be put in a small space on a computer disk that years ago would have seemed impossible. So, this is also very possible since the Lord is doing it.

God created the material for the earth and created the 1st, 2nd, and 3rd heaven where He placed his <u>spinning</u> power. The earth was not rotating or moving. Indeed, the earth was in no shape to do anything. It had nothing to hold it together. If it tried to spin in this condition, water and matter would make a muddy mess all over the universe. <u>The spinning power keeps the matter in one location.</u> God didn't create Christ's power in the 3rd heaven, because it has always existed. God did create the space in the 2nd heaven where the firmament would be placed on the second day. The Spirit of God has made a way for the atom "and a way for the lightning" (Job 28:26). Both the atom and lightning have electromagnetism.

At this point, the earth had material or matter and may have been mixed with water, but it had no form. The word "void" refers to the atomic structure, which was not present.

"And he is before all things, and by him all things consist" (Col 1:17). Christ's power has to be spinning to keep the material that makes up the universe in one place. If his power were absent for even one microsecond, everything would vaporize. "He maketh a path to shine after him" (Job 41:32). The power of the Holy Spirit has gone around over the same path so many times that the path shines.

Scripture says the universe was created in one second. "I have declared the former things from the beginning; and they went forth out of my mouth, and I showed them; I did them suddenly, and they came to pass" (Isaiah 48:3). "By the word of the Lord were the heavens made; and all the host of them by the breath of his mouth. For he spake, and it was done; he commanded, and it stood fast (Psalm 33:6,9). We can shout in a split second, so naturally God can and did.

THE FIRST MICROSECOND
(1000 microseconds = one second)

Genesis 1: 1 and the first 1/3 of 2 says, "In the beginning God created the heaven and the earth. And the earth was without form, and void." Since God is light, (1 John 1:5), He had to create darkness. Isaiah 45:7 says, "I form the light and create darkness." Since darkness was created in verse 2, light, electromagnetism, was also formed at the outer edge of the 2nd heaven at the same time. God placed the deep – a combination of His power and electromagnetism – all the way from the outer edge of the second heaven, inward to the center of the earth. By verse 3, microseconds later, the electromagnetism was planted in the atoms of the earth.

What we are seeing here at creation is that <u>the power of God spinning around heaven and earth at 10^{23} times per second just as electrons spin around the proton in an atom at 10^{23} times per second</u>. He transferred the pattern of the spinning power instantly to the atoms in Gen.1:3 when He said "Let there be light", (the atomic structure or electromagnetism). This speed is supported by the observation that some pulsar stars are rotating at 24,000 RPM.

God caused light to go into 2 different directions. "By what way is the light parted...?" (Job 38:24). After making at least one revolution around the universe following Christ's power in the 3rd heaven, light (electromagnetism) split into 2 parts. Part of it continues circling the universe and the second part dropped instantly to the earth, "Drop down, ye heavens...let the earth open..." (Isaiah 45:8). These verses are saying that the spinning plenum and power (electromagnetism) are transferred instantly to the atoms in the earth during the first part of the first second of the existence of heaven and earth. The earth is open to receive the power. The supporting verse is Psalm 68:8 "The earth shook, heavens dropped at the presence of God." Christ's power orbiting the universe maintains the atoms in the earth. If His power stopped, the universe would vaporize instantly. The electrons in the atom instantly began orbiting the proton at the same speed as Christ's power orbits the universe.

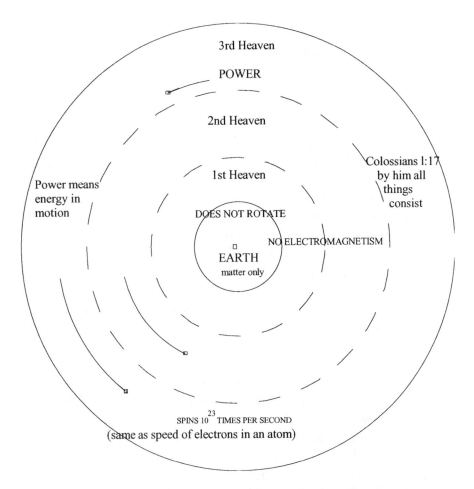

Note Zechariah 12:1: "The Lord stretcheth forth the heavens and layeth the foundation of the earth..." Here is a striking picture of how God stretched the electromagnetism and speed of his power in the 3rd heaven, *inward* to the atoms of the earth, which are its basic building blocks.

The earth now has atomic structure. The electromagnetism from the 3rd heaven has now reached the earth. The difference in time from start to finish is about 153 microseconds. The earth is complete and capable of rotating, but the power of God has already spun billions of times in the third heaven, keeping the material making up the earth in place

Proverbs 25:2 says that "It is the glory of God to conceal a thing, but the glory of kings is to search things out." A 3rd heaven containing spinning power, would qualify better than anything else, as being concealed and yet giving glory to God. The implication of "to search" is that, by investigating scripture, it is possible to know about the physical universe now.

God planted His spinning power, located in the 3rd heaven, into the atoms of the earth, giving meaning to Isaiah 51:16 "...I have covered thee in the shadow of mine hand, that I may plant the heavens, and lay the foundations of the earth..." So, this divine spinning power, which is upward, is the pattern used to produce many spinning electrons in the atom, downward. Likewise, when we have an atom, with the electrons spinning around the proton, we know it came from God's spinning power around the earth.

Ezekiel 1:27 says "...from the appearance of his loins upward, and from the appearance of his loins even downward..." There is only one place to plant anything, and that's in the earth.

God's power in the 3rd heaven (a gigantic *generator*) supplies the 1st and 2nd heaven and the earth with electromagnetism. Note Psalm 104:2, "...Who coverest *thyself* with light, as *with* a garment: who stretchest out the heavens like a curtain." In other words, electromagnetism covers everything under it like a garment. In Job 36:29, 30, we read "...of His tabernacle? Behold, He spreadeth His light upon it." The footnote says "light" is lightning. The tabernacle includes everything in the universe. So the picture is one of God spreading His lightning or electromagnetism in the tabernacle or heavens inward to the center of the earth.

"O Wheel" – Ezekiel 10:13, i.e., (O spinning plenum, firmament and Power of God) – This is a depiction of God's great, awesome, magnificent speed demonstrations. Note, 1 Corinthians 1:28, "God chose things which are not, to bring to nought things that are." The Pulpit Commentary says, "things of which men conceived as not existing." The "wheels" chart gives this verse literal meaning. "All scripture is given by inspiration of God and is profitable for ...correction...." (2 Timothy 3:16)

Creation's Tiny Mystery
by Robert V. Gentry   *The Genesis Rocks* 2?
Psalms 33:9 - "...he commanded, and it stood fast"

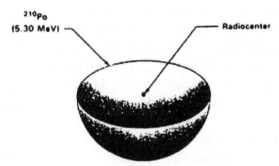

²¹⁰Po
(5.30 MeV) —   — Radiocenter

²¹⁰Po HALO CROSS SECTION

(²¹⁰Po half-life ≈ 138.4 days)

(²¹⁰Pb half-life ≈ 22 years)

Figure 2.1   ²¹⁰Po Halo Cross Section
Idealized three-dimensional illustration of a ²¹⁰Po halo obtained by slicing the halo
through the center. Each halo ring is identified by the appropriate isotope and its
alpha energy in MeV (Million electron Volts).

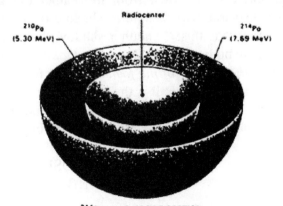

Radiocenter

²¹⁰Po   ²¹⁴Po
(5.30 MeV) —   — (7.69 MeV)

²¹⁴Po HALO CROSS SECTION

(²¹⁴Po half-life ≈ 164 microseconds)

(²¹⁴Pb half-life ≈ 26.8 minutes)

Figure 2.2   ²¹⁴Po Halo Cross Section
Idealized three-dimensional illustration of a ²¹⁴Po halo obtained by slicing the halo
through the center. Each halo ring is identified by the appropriate isotope and its
alpha energy in MeV (Million electron Volts).

God is omnipotent, omnipotent, and omnipresent. One cannot cut a region of space so small that God's power therein is not infinite. Hence, God is a plenum, which means that He rules space, every part of which is full of matter. Plenum means an infinitely dense medium.

God's power or plenum spinning in the 3rd heaven would make physical sense of Jeremiah 30:23 because a "continuing whirlwind" would last longer than an hour and turn faster than once a day. *The continuing whirlwind started at the first second of creation and has never stopped.* The coasts of the earth could only have meaning as in the drawing; looking at the earth from outside the universe. Habakkuk 3:4: "...the hiding of his power". His power really is hid behind the extremely dense rotating firmament making the verse have literal meaning. The word "whirlwind" should mean the same now as then.

Three verses say God's power, is in the whirlwind; Job 38:1; 40:6: "... the Lord answered Job out of the whirlwind". Then Nahum 1:3: "...the Lord hath his way in the whirlwind". This could be a regular whirlwind on the ground and/or *His power spinning in the 3rd heaven.* "His way" indicates movement and speed.

James 1:17 says "Every good gift and every perfect gift is from above, and cometh down from the Father of lights, with whom there is no variableness, neither shadow of turning." The Pulpit Commentary has this: "...neither shadow that is cast by turning of the heavenly bodies." *This is saying that a shadow on the earth is caused by the turning of the firmament, as it carries the sun, moon and stars around daily.* It is the intervening object, which is on the earth, and is between the sun and earth that makes the shadow. Since it is not turning, the earth is not spinning.

THE FIRST 164 MICROSECONDS
Genesis 1: 3

[David Bergman, 1157 W. Mill Drive, Kenesaw, GA 30152-5416, a speaker at creation meetings, believes that the first chapter of Ezekiel could be about the atom.]

DOMINION

"Knowest thou the ordinances of the heaven? Canst thou set the dominion thereof in the earth?" (Job 38:33). Ordinances means – "act of arranging, put in order, direction;" all having to do with *movement* – thus the heavens (or the firmament), are moving and turning. "Dominion" means sphere of influence, control, or authority. So how does heaven control the earth? The only way to understand heaven is to look at the atoms of the earth. Inside the atom we see that electrons orbit the proton. The proton, in the center, does not spin. Therefore, the way the atom works comes from the operation of heaven. So heaven, the firmament with the sun, moon and stars enclosed, revolves around the earth daily.

Job 38:33 supports Isaiah 45:8, p4. Every verse has a mate.

The Glory of God orbited the earth once a day for the first 3 days providing the light for the evening and morning. It established the pattern for the sun to follow on the fourth day, moving from east to west, as does the sun now.

LIGHT

Ecclesiastes 12:2 – "While the sun, or the light, or the moon, or the stars, be not darkened..." The sun, moon and stars each have physical structure. Since "light" is included in the group, *it also has structure.* It is a particle and it is electromagnetism. Psalm 74:16 says "...thou hast prepared the light and the sun." Light or electromagnetism, is different than the luminescence of the sun. Psalm 97:11 states: "Light is sown...." Only things that have structure are sown. The only place to sow anything, including electromagnetism, is in the earth. The universe and atoms in the earth are maintained by the power in Christ's word.

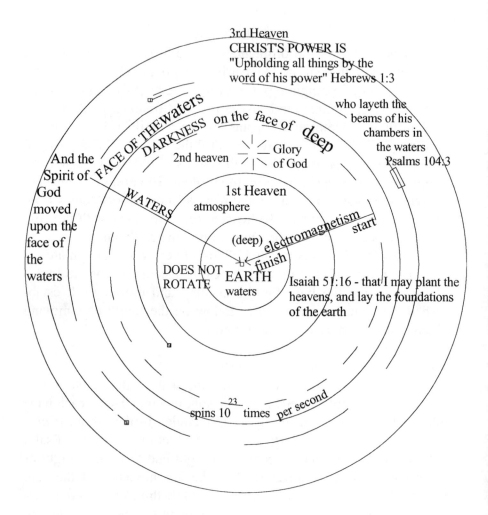

3rd Heaven
CHRIST'S POWER IS
"Upholding all things by the
word of his power" Hebrews 1:3

FACE OF THE waters

DARKNESS on the face of deep

2nd heaven

Glory
of God

who layeth the
beams of his
chambers in
the waters
Psalms 104:3

And the
Spirit of
God
moved
upon the
face of
the
waters

WATERS

1st Heaven
atmosphere

(deep)

electromagnetism

start

DOES NOT
ROTATE

EARTH
waters

finish

Isaiah 51:16 - that I may plant the
heavens, and lay the foundations
of the earth

23
spins 10 times per second

Chapter 3

GALILEO VERSUS THE GEOCENTRIC THEORY OF THE UNIVERSE

This article shows in detail how the change from geocentricity to heliocentrism occurred. It was copied and condensed from a 46-page pamphlet from: BRITONS CATHOLIC LIBRARY, by Martin Gwynne, Woodbrook House, Kilanne, Enniscorthy, Co., Wexforth, Ireland. I didn't copy the appendix, which was another 46 pages, but all 92 pages are available, free.

Let's examine geocentricity. "Not with me you won't," I can imagine some readers saying. It has already been solved 400 years ago plus I do not have the background knowledge necessary. However carefully we were to read what you have to say, we should be unable to form a judgment about who was right and who was wrong.

New subjects are seldom easy at first, and this is especially true where the little that one has been taught about them is wrong. No scientific principles are involved which are not logical and easily grasped by applying common sense or, in the case of false ones exposed, equally easily seen to be illogical.

Ether, which can neither by seen, tasted, smelled, touched nor weighted, is the substance of which all space beyond the atmosphere consists. Sound exists as a disturbance in the air. What air is to sound is exactly what ether is to light waves, electricity, magnetism, radio waves and gravity. Each particle of ether moves slightly out of position causing a wave, just as each drop of water does when a wave travels across the sea. The existence of ether must be true above the atmosphere, because waves must be waves of something.

Is there any identification of where one fixed point of the universe, if it exists, truly is? There are two viewpoints from which the question can be examined. The first is scientific and the second is religious.

Ever since heliocentrism was adopted as fact by the scientific community, attempts have been made to prove it. Some of them should have worked. Remarkably, not only has not one of them produced the proof, but the results of all of them are consistent with the hypothesis that the earth is at rest.

Unlike science, which had to prove itself, "Relativity" was not required to prove itself. All that the experiments show is that there are forces which act on bodies in motion relative to each other, and that either the earth is rotating or the inertial field of the universe is rotating round the earth.

The most difficult phenomenon to reconcile with a geocentric universe is the stationary satellite at 22,300 miles above the earth. According to the heliocentric theory, they travel at the same speed as the earth rotates and centrifugal force holds them up. If neither the satellite nor the earth rotate according to the geocentric theory, what holds them up? It is perfectly possible, and not an illogical concept, that the rotation of distant masses can generate gravitational field that exactly equals the centrifugal field. A top-ranking Viennese scientist, Professor Hans Thirring, demonstrated satisfactorily in the early part of this century that "distant rotary masses cause forces to appear which are similar to the centrifugal forces."

Geocentricity is not rejected because of any incompatibility between geocentricity and experience, but solely because geocentricity is philosophical untenable. If it were not for the need felt by some scientists to rebel against the Bible, attempts to look beyond geocentric cosmology would never have occurred.

The Michelson-Morley experiment had left the heliocentric theory of the universe floundering and in a state from which - if it were not to be abandoned, which was unthinkable - it must be rescued; but so definite was the direction in which the Michelson-Morley experiment pointed that either heliocentricity had to go and geocentricity be allowed to return, or the whole of science had to go. Foucault's pendulum and the Coriolis effect only demonstrate relative motion and do not demonstrate which, if either, of the two objects is at rest. It is an essential part of Christian theology that the continued existence of every particle in the universe depends on God's continuing, for every second of time, to sustain it. Yet where in Genesis, or for that matter in the whole Bible, is there even the faintest hint, that God, having created the Earth in the beginning, demoted it on the fourth day to one spinning corkscrewing lump of matter out of many? The comfortable and reassuring bounded universe of tradition was replaced by a universe allegedly infinite in size.

The first contact between Galileo and Kepler took place in 1597. Galileo's first explicit public pronouncement in favor of the Copernican system was made in 1613. For sixteen years he not only taught, in his lectures, the old astronomy according to Ptolemy, but expressly repudiated Copernicus. Galileo spent the spring of 1611 in Rome. Astronomers at the College were now entirely converted. Galileo developed the argument that certain statement in the Bible should not be taken literally because they were couched in language "according to the capacity of the common people who are rude and unlearned."

In a breathtaking passage he queried the title and authority of theology as queen of the sciences and grossly misrepresented the attitude of the Church to propositions which contradict th apparent meaning of passage in the Bible as follows: "And as to the propositions which are stated but not rigorously demonstrated, anything contrary to the Bible involved by them must be held undoubtedly false and should be proved so by every possible means."

Now this was demonstrably not the attitude of the Church. "Propositions which are stated but not rigorously demonstrated," such as the Copernican system itself, were not condemned outright, if they seemed to contradict Holy Scripture; they were merely relegated to the rank of "working hypotheses" (where they rightly belong), with an implied: "wait and see; if you bring proof, then, but only then, we shall have to reinterpret Scripture in the light of this necessity." But Galileo did not want to bear the burden of proof: for the crux of the matter is, as will be seen, that he had no proof. Therefore, firstly, he conjured up an artificial black-or-white alternative, by pretending that a proposition must either be accepted or outright condemned. The purpose of this sleight of hand becomes evident from the next sentence:

"Now if truly demonstrated physical conclusions need not be subordinated to biblical passages, but the latter must rather by shown not to interfere with the former, then <u>before a physical</u>

<u>proposition is condemned it must be shown to be not rigorously demonstrated</u> - and this is to be done not be those who hold the proposition to be true, but by those who judge it to be false. This seems very reasonable and natural, for those who believe an argument to be false may much more easily find the fallacies in it than men who consider it to be true and conclusive..."

The burden of proof has been shifted. The crucial words are those underlined by me. It is no longer Galileo's task to prove the Copernican system, but the theologians" task to disprove it. If they don't, their case will go by default, and Scripture must be reinterpreted.

He implied that the truth of the system was rigorously demonstrated. It is all so subtly done that it has escaped the attention to this day.

For the next eighteen years Galileo lived honored and unmolested.

In 1615 a Neapolitan monk produced an unofficial definition of the Church's attitude to Copernicus. It included the following:

If there were a real proof that the Sun is in the center of the universe, that the Earth is in the third sphere, and that the Sun does not go around the Earth, but the Earth round the Sun, then we should have to proceed with great circumspection in explaining passages of Scripture which appear to teach the contrary. But none has been shown to me. To demonstrate that the appearance are saved by assuming the sun at the center and the earth in the heavens is not the same thing as to demonstrate that in fact the sun is in the center and the earth is in the heavens. The burden of proof had been placed back where it belonged, on Galileo. He had to supply the required proof, or agree that the Copernican system should be treated as a working hypothesis.

How could Galileo manage to refuse to produce proof and at the same time demand that the matter should be treated as if proven? The solution of the dilemma was to pretend that he had the proof, but to refuse to produce it, on the grounds that his opponents were too stupid, anyway, to understand.

Galileo now did everything in his power to provoke a showdown.

On February 23rd, 1616, the Theological Experts of the Holy

Office gave their opinion on the two following propositions submitted to them:

1. The sun is the center of the world and wholly immovable of local motion.
2. The earth is not the center of the world nor immovable, but moves as a whole, also with diurnal motion.

The Theological Experts declared the first proposition to be: "foolish and absurd, philosophically and formally heretical inasmuch as it expressly contradicts the doctrine of Holy Scriptures in many passages, both in their liter meaning and according to the general interpretation of the Fathers and Doctors." The second proposition was declared "to deserve the like censure in philosophy, and as regards theological truth, to be at least erroneous in faith." The Experts" verdict was overruled under pressure of the more enlightened Cardinals; it was only published in full seventeen years later. Instead of it, on March 5th, the General Congregation of the Index issued a more moderate decree, in which the fatal word "heresy" did not appear. The document had consequences which are still felt today. It represents the crack in the wall which led to the falling apart of Science and Faith.

The experts" talked of heresy, the decree did not. The Experts" Opinion became known to the public only in 1633. It remained a judicial opinion and not binding on the members of the Church. Accordingly, the immobility of the earth never became an article of faith, nor the immobility of the sun, a heresy.

Chapter 4

THE REVOLVING HEAVEN

GEOCENTRICITY EXTENDED TO INCLUDE MORE VERSES.

(No one that believes in geocentricity accepts numbers 3-7 of the following proposal. This is my personal opinion.)

[THE EARTH]

1. DOES NOT ROTATE

In the beginning the earth did not spin.

2. DOES NOT ROTATE - AT THE PRESENT TIME

The earth continues standing still until midway through the tribulation period. The firmament, enclosing the sun, moon and stars, rotates daily around the earth. The firmament must rotate to exist.

3. ROTATES - LAST HALF OF TRIBULATION - Isaiah 13:13

God miraculously causes the firmament to instantly stop rotating and the earth to instantly begin rotating, to provide day and night. The world gets what it has always believed and which embarrasses God's word. The universe is unstable.

4. DOES NOT ROTATE - MILLENNIUM - Haggai 2:6,7

The earth does not rotate and the firmament does, which is normal and stable.

5. ROTATES - SATAN LOOSED - Hebrews 12:26,27

When Satan is loosed for a season, God shakes the heavens and the earth causing the firmament to stop its daily rotation and the earth to rotate.

6. NEITHER THE FIRMAMENT NOR THE EARTH ROTATE - JUDGMENT DAY

For judgment day God again shakes the heavens and earth. The firmament is stationary and now the earth stops.– Job 38:12,13

7. DAY AND NIGHT ROTATES

Day and night rotates forever inside the great gulf. Luke 16:26

****

John 3:12 says, "If I have told you of earthly things, and ye believe not, how shall ye believe, if I tell you of heavenly things?" Based on this statement, a second look at certain verses dealing with physical things is in order.

Isaiah 34:16, "...none (no verse) shall want her mate..." Every verse is explained or supported and made complete by another verse. Let's let our imagination run wild, if necessary, to stay <u>with</u> God as he leads.

1. THE EARTH DOES NOT ROTATE

Genesis 1:2 says "And the Spirit of God moved upon the face of the waters." Why? For what reason? The Spirit is accomplishing two tasks in this verse. In addition to the Spirit's work with the atom (See "The First Second" article), the Spirit of God is establishing a path for the firmament to follow (as explained below). If this is true, there must be another verse where the Spirit is physically moving. The mate is Mark 1:10, "...and the Spirit like a dove descending upon him." The Spirit physically moves in both verses for a very important reason. Isaiah 43:16 says, "Thus saith the Lord, which maketh a <u>way</u> in the sea, and a <u>path</u> in the mighty waters." Likewise, the Spirit of God has made a <u>way</u> for the atom "a way for the lightning" (Job 28:26) and a <u>path</u> for the firmament.

Does the earth spin or does the sun orbit the earth? The discussion of the earth ends in verse 3. This question is partially settled in Gen. 1:4,5 where it says "And God saw the light, that it was good: and God divided the light from the darkness. And God called the light Day, and the darkness he called Night. And the evening and the morning were the first day." God made a distinct division between light and darkness on the first day. Each part of the earth had the morning light during the first day. The light had to move around the earth to do this. This light is different and separate from the sun, "thou hast prepared the light and the sun," (Psalm 74:16). The morning and evening are a direct result of the movement of the prepared light around the earth on the first day. God is writing to us about basic, fundamental scientific law. So the Spirit of God started a path for the prepared light to follow even before the dry land of the earth appeared or the firmament was established! (The "prepared light" reappears again after

188

judgment day).

"And God said, Let there be a firmament in the midst of the waters, and let it divide the waters from the waters. And God made the firmament, and divided the waters which were under the firmament from the waters which were above the firmament: and it was so" Genesis 1:6,7. The word "let" in Webster's dictionary means, to give opportunity to, enter or pass. In other words, to move. The phrase "let it divide" therefore says, "to give opportunity to" the firmament to divide the waters from the waters. The firmament moves or spins and divides the upper waters from the lower waters.

Did the firmament or God divided the waters? (Ezekiel 30:23) "And I (the Lord God) will scatter the Egyptians among the nations..." God did not, himself, scatter the Egyptians, but used the Babylons to do it. In the same way God, did not by a miracle separate the waters, but used the firmament to divide the waters. The firmament does not divide the waters by standing still doing nothing, but by spinning. The firmament separates the waters just as a separator separates the cream from the milk. The firmament is simply following the path laid out by the Spirit of God. Exodus 14:16 says, "...and stretch out thine hand over the sea, and divide it..." Moses moved his hand and divided the sea. Likewise, the firmament began revolving around the earth dividing the waters and has never stopped!

Psalm 119:147 – The morning comes because the sun moves around a stationary earth. The belief in heliocentrism stops the dawning regardless of what the word says.

Proverbs 28:9 – "He that turneth away his ear from hearing the law, even his prayer shall be abomination." Why would the word "turneth" be used, when God could have said, "He that refuseth to listen to the law?" The word "turneth" is used because the whole problem is: what is turning, the earth spinning daily on its axis or the firmament revolving daily around a non moving earth? Next, what law is referred to? There are food laws, laws of sacrifice and solar system laws. The law did not begin in Genesis 12, but in Genesis 1. With a lump in my throat, it looks like: if we don't believe in geocentricity, our prayers are damaged. This is a terrible accusation. Is this a test of fellowship? No. It is simply information that we need to be aware of.

"Where is the <u>way</u> where light dwelleth?" (Job 38:19). It doesn't say "place" where light dwelleth because light is always moving. The source of light, either the prepared light or the sun, is always orbiting the earth. Beginning with the 2nd day, the firmament stays in step with the already orbiting, moving, prepared light, and starts revolving around the earth. The principal of geocentricity and the law of the solar system are established on the second day. The word "way" is also used in Isaiah 43:16, "Thus saith the LORD, which maketh a way in the sea, and a path in the mighty waters;" because there are swift moving currents in the oceans.

Verse 15 and 17 both say "to give light <u>upon the earth</u>" which emphases the final result of all the activity and rotating lights in the heavens. Sunlight identifies the day. The earth stays in one place and does not turn to receive the light; supported by Deut. 11:21 "days of heaven <u>upon the earth</u>." In verse 16, the greater light, the sun, takes the place of, or surrounds the prepared light. God's dividing the greater light from the lesser light only confirms what was already done the vs. 5.

Genesis 2:4 says, "These are the generations of the heavens and of the earth when they were created, in the day that the Lord God made the earth and the heavens." The third definition of "generation" according to Webster's Dictionary is that it means formation of a geometric figure by <u>motion</u> of another. The dictionary also says that one geometric figure or shape is a circle. "Generations" applied here, means moving in a circle.

The earth, by spinning, is <u>not</u> daily making a geometric figure or shape. It is staying in one spot. Remember, the verse is talking about motion "in the day" not yearly. The context of chapter two is one day. So, only the heavens are making a geometric figure or circle by orbiting the earth. Paraphrasing the verse we have: "These are the motion of the heavens around the earth." Every phrase [the earth and the heavens] has its mate: (Isaiah 34:16). "Of old hast thou laid the foundation of the earth: and the heavens are the work of thy hands."(Psa 102:25). The earth, on a foundation doesn't spin and God started the heavens revolving with his hands.

Genesis 1:14 says, "And God said, Let there be lights in the firmament of the heaven to divide the day from the night: and let them be for signs, and for seasons, and for days, and years." What ever does the dividing does the moving. The sun does the moving. The sun could not move only to determine the season and years, and the spinning earth to determine the day. God "created darkness," Isaiah 45:7, as a background of heavenly darkness in order for the light of the moving sun to serve its function of indicating "days." We are not talking about the earth until the next verse, so the sun moves to determine the seasons and <u>days</u> and years. Verse 15 says, "And let them be for lights in the firmament of the heaven to give light upon the earth, and it was so." The sun divides the light from darkness and gives light to determine the day on the earth, not a spinning earth. The greater light, the rotating sun, determines the seasons, days, and years. Either the lights determine all of these, or none of them according to the verse. Again, these verses are foundational to the rest of scripture. God is telling us exactly how the universe is set up.

Psalm 19:2,4 says, "Day unto day uttereth speech, and night unto night showeth knowledge. Their line is gone through out all the earth..." Webster's dictionary says "line" means: direction of something in motion and "unto" means: action, continuance, movement and direction. If "day unto day" is moving, certainly "day and night" would be moving. The "day" says that it is rotating and the night shows rotation.

"Thou liftest me up to the wind; thou causest me to ride upon it..." (Job 30:22). The wind is moving and the earth is not spinning. Psalm 68:4 says "...him (God) that rideth upon the heavens..." Amos 2:15 says "...he that rideth the horse..." Both the heavens and the horse move, whereas "It is he (God) that sitteth upon the circle of the earth (Isa. 40:22) and "The LORD sitteth upon the flood (Psa 29:10). Isaiah 66:2 says "...the earth is my footstool..." Whoever heard of a spinning footstool? The daily rotating firmament (heaven) enclosing the sun causes the division line between day and night to move. The heavens are not God's footstool, nor does God ride on the earth. "To him that rideth upon the heavens of heaven" (Psalm 68:33). The heaven (firmament) is revolving around the earth.

"They know not, neither will they understand; they walk on

in darkness: all the foundations of the earth are out of course" (Psalm 82:5)." Psalm 74:17 says, "Thou hast set all the borders of the earth." It isn't 'borders of the 'sun, moon and stars' (universe). 'Borders' keep things inside. The earth cannot move through the borders, so the earth does not revolve around the sun. According to Marshal Hall, 67 verses say the earth is not moving. See: www.fixedearth.com/sixty-seven%20references.htm. There are only 5 verses that say the earth is moving and all are in a negative context or a context of judgment.

Job 38:4,6 says, "Where wast thou when I laid the foundations of the earth?...Whereupon are the foundations thereof fastened?" Both the heavens (2 Samuel 22:8) and the world (2 Samuel 22:16) have foundations; but only the foundations of the earth are fastened so that the earth cannot turn or spin.

If the earth were spinning, it would make meaningless the following group of verses.

ECCLESIASTES 1:4-7
[4] One generation passeth away...another...cometh
[5] The sun also ariseth...goeth down
[6] The wind goeth...returneth
[7] All the rivers run...return again.

We are to take things in context. We know the generations, wind and rivers actually move, so the sun also literally, physically moves being carried daily around the earth by the rotating firmament.

"Circuit" means to go around. Ecclesiastes 1:6 "...and the wind returneth again according to his circuits." We know the wind is blowing, the earth is not turning. The heaven is also moving, "...and he walketh in the circuit of heaven." (Job 22:14).

The word mystery, or mysteries, is listed 28 times in a concordance. It refers to the mystery of Christ, the kingdom of God or spiritual things. "Mystery" does not refer to anything physical. God has told us more details concerning the physical universe than we think He has.

2. DOES NOT ROTATE - AT THE PRESENT TIME

The earth has not rotated since the day of creation nor will it rotate until midway through the tribulation period.

The firmament carries the sun around the earth faster than the moon because the moon is closer to the earth, the center of the universe. "If I beheld the sun when it shined, or the moon walking in brightness" (Job 31:26). The sun never walks, but runs; "...the sun. Which...rejoiceth as a strong man to run a race" (Psalm 19:4,5).

We aren't living in the millennium with the historical records that will then be available to be examined, of what will happened to the physical universe. We must believe now, revealed truths about the physical universe, that God has written in scripture. Christians living in the millennium will ask themselves, "How could those living in the church age have missed the meaning of verses that we clearly understand now?"

The drawing below, by R G Elmendorf, 314 Oak Road, Bairford, PA 15006, shows the sun (S) orbiting the earth (E), which is in the center of the universe. (He does not necessarily agree or disagree with this or other articles.)

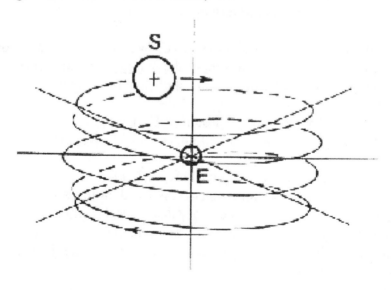

3. ROTATES - LAST HALF OF TRIBULATION

In Genesis 1:1-3 God provides many physical details, which occurred in less than one second, from "Creation's Tiny Mystery" by Robert Gentry. The end time is the same. God as "a faithful Creator," 1 Peter 4:19, gives a blow-by-blow description of events, again happening in one second.

Isaiah 13:13 says, "Therefore I will shake the heavens, and the earth shall remove out of her place, in the <u>wrath</u> of the Lord of hosts, and in the day of his fierce anger." God is angry with the wicked and gives them heliocentrism, which they have always wanted because it embarrasses God's word. The universe is now, not in a stable condition, it is not reality and is against God's word. Without God's supernatural power to hold it together, the universe would instantly <u>vaporize</u>.

Isaiah 2:19 says, "And they shall go into the holes of the rocks, and into the caves of the earth, for fear of the LORD, and for the glory of his majesty, when he ariseth to shake terribly the earth." The wicked try to hide from God.

Amos 1:2 says, "And he said, The Lord will roar from Zion..." Psalm 33:9 says, "For he spake, and it was done..." As the universe was created when God spoke, surely something must have happened when He <u>roared</u>.

There is a collision in outer space! The biggest and most colossal wreck of all time occurs in the universe. The sun and moon, which weigh next to nothing compared to the firmament; instantly hit the massive firmament. Isaiah 30:26 - "...the light of the moon shall be as the light of the sun and the light of the sun shall be seven-fold, as the light of seven days..." As in any crash that we know of, there often is an explosion and a flash of light.

The only way this could happen and make sense of these verses is for God to miraculously, instantly stop the firmament. Even though the firmament is extremely dense; it reacts instantly to any movement within it, so the sun and moon move freely through it in their own individual orbits. But when the rotating firmament abruptly stops, there will be the most colossal wreck of all time in the universe. The sun and moon, which weigh next to nothing compared to the firmament; instantly hit, at full speed, the

194

dense, massive, heavy, <u>now</u> *immovable* firmament. God not only

Frame 1   Frame 2   Frame 3

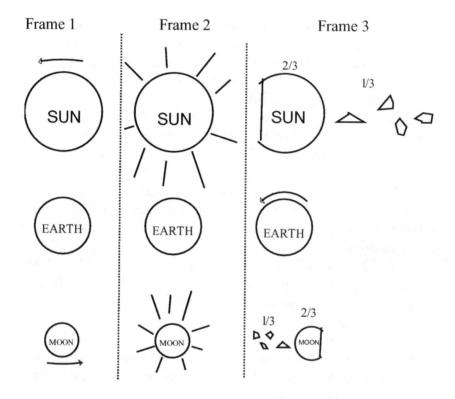

instantly stops the firmament from spinning, and instantly stops the firmament from reacting to any movement within it, causing the crash. So the firmament, traveling at many thousands of miles per hour, stops, causing the sun, moon and stars, also going thousands of miles per hour, to collide, with the firmament.

Immediately after the crash, just as people black out after a collision, so does the sun and moon. Isaiah 13:10 says "...the sun shall be darkened in his going forth, and the moon shall not cause her light to shine." The rotating firmament had been orbiting the earth carrying the sun and moon. The sun and moon had been moving, (going forth). Now, both are temporarily blacked out. Acts 2:20 and Joel 2:31 both say, "The sun shall be turned into darkness, and the moon into blood..." Revelation 6:12 – "... the sun became black as sackcloth of hair, and the moon became as blood." Just as humans are covered with blood after a wreck, the moon shows the effect of the collision by a red color.

As the firmament instantly stops rotating, with the resulting crash of the sun, moon and stars into it, and the earth instantly begins rotating to provide day and night. When the daily turning of the firmament is "taken away", Daniel 12:11, and actually, really, does stop turning, the earth will immediately begin to rotate daily. One or the other has to turn to have day and night. Genesis 8:22 says, "While the earth remaineth.... day and night shall not cease". Isaiah 2:19 says, "...for fear of the Lord, and for the glory of his majesty, when he ariseth to shake terribly the earth." And verse 21 has, "...to go into the clefts of the rock...when he ariseth to shake terribly the earth." These 2 verses deal with the earth starting to spin. This happens in the middle of the tribulation period, when the anti-christ revels himself, the world will then know what it is really like to have the earth spinning! The world wanted heliocentrism to discredit scripture, and will now fully reap what it sowed.

The earth starts rotating and the sun stops. "The pillars of heaven tremble and are astonished at his reproof" (Job 26:11). The pillars of both the earth and the firmament tremble as the rotation switches from the firmament to the earth. The firmament has always rotated daily since creation and is "astonished" at being stopped! These verses fit very well in this sequence of events, make good physical sense and God had a very good reason for writing the verses. The stars were sealed and could not give light as Revelation 8:12 says, "...and the third part of the sun was smitten, and third part of the moon, and the third part of the stars, so as the third part of them was darkened, and the day shone not for a third part of it, and the night likewise". Being "smitten" changes the lighting arrangement for the earth. It takes the sun, moon and stars perhaps 8 hours, 1/3 of a day, to recover from this catastrophe and then can only shine 2/3's as bright as before. There will be less light during the day. The evening light will last longer. Zechariah 14:6, "...that the light shall not be clear nor dark." Vs. 7 says, "...not day, nor night: but it shall come to pass, that at evening time, it shall be light." The main part of the sun, two thirds of it, and the pieces making up the other 1/3, which are some distance behind, do not move. The earth rotates and 2/3 of the sun appears to go down, followed by the other 1/3 of the sun. The same is true for the moon. This new lighting system remains through the rest of the tribulation period, the millennium and when Satan is loosed.

(With the firmament not rotating and the earth spinning, the universe is operating the opposite of normal and is in a diseased state. It is like an anaerobic organism, which lives only in the absence of oxygen. An aerobic organism lives only in the presence of oxygen.)

4. EARTH DOES NOT ROTATE - MILLENIUM

"For thus saith the Lord of hosts; Yet once, it is a little while, and I will shake the heavens, and the earth...and I will fill this house with glory, saith the Lord of hosts" (Haggai 2:6,7.) To start the millennium the Lord shakes heaven and earth to return the earth to its normal stationary non-moving position and the heaven (or firmament) revolving around the earth. God is not angry this time, because he is dealing with his saints. A slightly dimmer day and a night that is not totally dark continues the same as during the last half of the tribulation period.

5. EARTH ROTATES - SATAN LOOSED

At the end of the millennium "...he (Satan) must be loosed a little season" (Rev. 20:3). This is a second tribulation period of perhaps three or four months. Christ has ruled the earth, but now it is time for evil to have one final testing of those that lived during the millennium.

"Yet once more I shake not the earth only, but also heaven. And this word, Yet once more, signifieth the removing of those things that are shaken, as of things that are made, that those things which cannot be shaken may remain" (Hebrews 12:26, 27). The phrase "yet once more" shows that God has shaken the heavens and earth at different times in the past. Once again, the earth rotates and heaven (or firmament) is stationary and in an unstable condition. The word "more" is added now compared to millennium to show another step in the process toward the end. Physical things and the wicked will be removed.

Now, Matthew 24:29 says, "Immediately after the tribulation of those days shall the sun be darkened, and the moon shall not give her light, and the stars shall fall from heaven..."

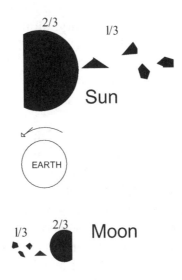

Sun

Moon

Total darkness just before judgment day? How long will it last? Perhaps this is where Daniel 12:11,12 applies; the difference between 1335 and 1290 days is 45 days. Our merciful God knows that millions of lost souls are in a rut. By slowing down activity, God hopes to cause them to do some serious thinking and repent. Imagine the situation. The only light available will be the city light plant, headlights, flashlights, and candles. Food could be harder to locate and driving more difficult. Any minor trouble would be big trouble.

6. NEITHER THE FIRMAMENT NOR THE EARTH ROTATE – JUDGMENT DAY

"The Lord shall roar from on high, and utter his voice from his holy habitation; he shall mightily roar upon his habitation; he shall give a shout...A noise shall come even to the ends of the earth..." (Jeremiah 25:30,31). The Lord shouts and Christ, as the "dayspring," takes "...hold of the ends of the earth that the wicked might be shaken out of it?" (Job 38:12,13). The spinning earth stops abruptly, shaking out the wicked from this last tribulation period. The 2nd heaven or firmament has already been motionless so only the earth, which has been spinning needs to be stopped.

Since the firmament is stationary, all the stars fall to the earth gently "all their host shall fall down, as the leaf falleth off from the vine..." (Isaiah 34:4). "And the stars of heaven fell unto the earth..." (Revelation 6:13). "And moreover I saw under the sun the place of judgment..." (Eccl. 3:16). Perhaps just above the earth is the place of judgment.

"And then shall appear the sign of the Son of man in heaven: and then shall all the tribes of the earth mourn, and they shall see the Son of man coming in the clouds of heaven with power and great glory" (Matthew 24:30). Both Psalm 18:9 and 2 Samuel 22:10 have, "He bowed the heavens also, and came down; and darkness was under his feet." "Bowed," suggests a little slower action than "dropped." The heavens dropped at the beginning of creation (First Second article, p. 6) and bowed, now, at the end. Joel 3:14-16 says, "Multitudes, multitudes in the valley of decision: for the day of the Lord is near in the valley of decision. The sun and the moon shall be darkened, and the stars shall withdraw their shining. The Lord also shall roar out of Zion, and utter his voice from Jerusalem; and the heavens and the earth shall shake..." This is the 3rd heaven.

Neither the firmament nor the earth are moving on Judgment Day. This is just the opposite of Joshua's Long Day, in which both the firmament and the earth were moving, and also, for the same period of time, one day!

The universe and earth are totally dark and standing still. Neither the sun nor moon nor any pieces of either one radiate any light: "the day of the Lord is darkness, and not light. Shall not the day of the Lord be darkness and not light? even very dark, and no brightness in it?" (Amos 5:18,20). What a contrast! Total darkness with Christ himself the only light. For the first time since the universe was created, there is no motion of any kind. God now has the attention of all the unsaved for judgment day.

"Light shall be dark in his tabernacle" (Job 18:6). The Lord's tabernacle is the universe (Psalm 19:4) and it is now dark.

[DAY AND NIGHT]
7. ROTATES

The new heaven and new earth are now in place. There is no light or sun, "...neither light of the sun..." (Rev. 22:5). "He hath compassed the waters with bounds, until the day and night come to an end" Job 26:10). The water is also gone, "...no more sea" (Rev. 21:1), so now, day and night, caused by the rotating sun, is finished. But, Rev. 20:10 says, "...tormented day and night for ever and ever. So is there to be day and night in eternity or not?

As the drawing shows, a great gulf in the shape of a sphere is inside the new earth, "...with a great gulf fixed" (Luke 16:26). The gulf totally seals hell, which is in the center of the new earth. (It could not be anywhere else, because that will be where heaven is and we are) The only way to have day and night is for there to be a rotation of some kind inside the new earth. Hell will be dark so how could "day" be included? Amos 5:8 has, "... and maketh the day dark with night..." So the day and night will rotate even though the day is dark. The irony of it all! Satan, after deceiving the world with heliocentrism, will have this continual, permanent, day and night rotation around him for all eternity, reminding him of his great deception! The universe began with the firmament rotating above the earth causing day and night and ends with a day-night rotation in the core of the earth. The new earth, great gulf and lake of fire do not rotate.

The location of hell is in the center of the new earth with

the great gulf enclosing and completely surrounding it. "And thou, Capernaum, which art exalted to heaven, shalt be thrust down to hell" (Luke 10:15). This city on the earth will be pushed down to hell. More support for this is: Ephesians 4:8-10, which says, "Wherefore he saith, When he ascended up on high, he led captivity captive, and gave gifts unto men. (Now that he ascended, what is it but that he also descended first into the lower parts of the earth? He that descended is the same also that ascended up far above all heavens, that he might fill all things.)" From the cross Christ descended down directly to hell.

The lost, who are confined to hell, have chosen not to have anything to do with God's word, so His word stops at the great gulf. These three verses make sense only from a physical point of view.

Rev. 20:10 has "...the lake of fire and brimstone..." yet Jude 13 says "...the blackness of darkness for ever." Fire gives light, so how does this correlate with darkness in hell? Perhaps they are in different locations, as the drawing shows.

From the "First Second" article, atoms have been in heaven and earth from just after the first few microseconds (Gen. 1:2) until the end. In the beginning the material for the earth was placed first and then the atomic structure was inserted into the material a few microseconds later. Now, at the end the material and the atomic structure both leave at the same time. Revelation 20:11 says, "...the earth and the heaven fled away; and there was found no place for them." The earth consisted of material or matter and the atomic structure. Unlike the beginning, both leave at the same time. This is shown in Jeremiah. The context of Jeremiah 4:19-28 is the end, not the beginning, with verse 23 saying, "I beheld the earth, and, lo, it was without form, and void; and the heavens, and they had no light." This verse is about the same as verse 2 at the beginning. The light in the heavens represents the atomic structure. With the light gone from the heavens, the atomic structure has left the earth along with all the matter. "The earth is utterly broken down, the earth is clean dissolved, the earth is moved exceedingly" (Isaiah 24:19).

2 Peter 3:12 has "...wherein the heavens being on fire shall be dissolved, and the elements shall melt with fervent heat?" The

elements, which are located in the firmament or first heaven, including the sun, moon and stars, all melt and fall to the earth burning it up, "...the earth also and the works therein shall be burned up" (2 Peter 3:10). Affirming this also is Psalms 46:6, "...the earth melted." Perhaps the elements cover the earth like the water covered the earth during Noah's flood. So the saved, when they are outside New Jerusalem on the new earth, may walk on the elements of the firmament! The new earth will also be vastly larger than the present earth because all the elements in the firmament cover it. Revelation 20:11 says, "the earth...fled away." The volume of the earth will 'fly' away when it expands to a tremendous size.

Rev. 21:18 says "...and the city was pure gold, like unto clear glass." As gold is one of the elements in the firmament, the gold that covers the city and streets could come from this final event. The gold will be clear and transparent (vs. 21).

Psalm 148:4 says, "Praise him, ye heavens of heavens, and ye waters that be above the heavens." "He hath also stablished them for ever and ever: he hath made a decree which shall not pass" (vs. 6). From this verse, the waters will exist for ever. However, Revelation 21:1 says, "there was no more sea" or the end of the existence of water.

So, is water to be in the new heaven or not?

Water represents the "Word of God" in scripture. As the present heaven is filled with the firmament and water (Gen. 1:7 and Psalm 148:4), the new heaven will be filled with God's word. God's word will be throughout the heavens and downward to the new earth. The saved will have complete access to scripture.

"Them" in Psalm 148:6, also includes the "sun and moon...stars of light" (vs. 3) as being in the new heaven. But, two verses say the opposite that the sun will not be in the new heaven. (Rev 22:5,23) "And there shall be no night there; and they need no candle, neither light of the sun; for the Lord God giveth them light: and they shall reign for ever and ever." "And the city had no need of the sun, neither of the moon, to shine in it: for the glory of God did lighten it, and the Lamb is the light thereof."

So, is the sun in the new heaven for eternity or not?

Notice two verses, "...thou hast prepared the light and the sun"

(Psalm 74:16). Since "the prepared light" is listed separate from the other two, it is a separate entity.

What then, is God telling us?

The "light" in Genesis 1:3 is the "prepared light" that orbited the earth for the first 3 days. When the sun was formed in verse 14, it surrounds and encloses the prepared light. The prepared light and the sun are interchangeable, both being in the same position, only at different times.

God's "prepared light" in some form similar to the sun will orbit the new earth for eternity, to emphasize the importance to us now, of geocentricity. The "prepared light" that provided light for the first 3 days, reappears to orbit the new earth for eternity. As "day and night" orbit hell for eternity, so the "prepared light" will orbit the new earth for eternity. Every verse is true with important information. "His seed shall endure for ever...as the sun before me. It shall be established for ever as the moon, and as a faithful witness in heaven." (Psalm 89:36,37) The "prepared light" or "a form" of the sun will always exist. The moon will be a witness in the new heaven that as the "prepared light" representing the sun orbits the new earth, so the sun orbits the present earth. "For the Lord God is a sun..." (Psalm 84:11). God knows very well what the sun is doing since creation and what the prepared light will do throughout eternity. "God is light" (1 John 1:5).

Daniel 12:3 says, "they that turn many to righteousness as the stars, for ever and ever." Some form of the stars will also be in the new heaven, perhaps to represent scripture verses, while the restored water represents the Word of God. (Rom. 9:17) "For the scripture saith unto Pharaoh, Even for this same purpose have I raised thee up, that I might shew my power in thee, and that my name might be declared throughout all the earth." This verse is quoting Exodus 9:16, which God himself personally said, "And in very deed for this cause have I raised thee up, for to shew in thee my power; and that my name may be declared throughout all the earth." This means that "scripture saith" agrees with "God saith" or the "Word of God." All the trustworthiness of God Himself rests upon all 31,175 verses of scripture.

Isaiah 60:1,2 says "...and gross darkness the people..." Gross means being glaringly, obviously, deficient in knowledge. Just

204

how bad is this? "....and there was a thick darkness in all the land of Egypt three days...They saw not one another, neither rose any from his place for three days..." (Exodus 10:22,23). Thick darkness is more physical and gross darkness has more to do with spiritual things. Imagine the physical problems: normal body functions plus thirst and hunger. And this is only thick darkness. The people are in even worse darkness, because they don't believe God's words. Scripture is obviously geocentric. Mankind is so blinded by science that very few can even look at the so-called proof of the earth spinning on its axis. The sun could orbit the non-moving earth or the earth could spin with the sun stationary: we see the same thing either way. When in doubt, we must choose God's opinion.

Adapted from "The Revelation Record" by Henry Morris, p.29

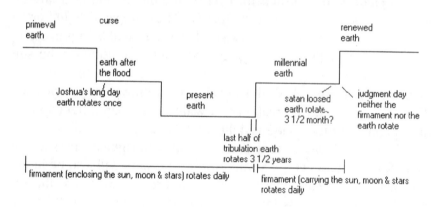

Gospel - Geocentricity

(Rom 10:15-18) And how shall they preach, except they be sent? as it is written, How beautiful are the feet of them that preach the gospel of peace, and bring glad tidings of good things. But they have not all obeyed the gospel. For Esaias saith, Lord, who hath believed our report? So then faith cometh by hearing, and hearing by the word of God. But I say, Have they not heard? Yes verily, <u>their sound went into all the earth, and their words unto the ends of the world</u>." The subject is the preaching of the gospel. "Their sound," the gospel, has moved over the earth. The footnote refers to Psalm 19:1-4, which says, "The heavens declare the glory of God; and the firmament showeth his handiwork. Day unto day uttereth speech, and night unto night showeth knowledge. There is no speech nor language, where their voice is not heard…and their words to the end of the world." What "words"? The firmament is saying that it is moving around the earth. "Day – night – day – night" is caused by the firmament (with the sun enclosed) revolving around a stationary earth daily. The gospel moves – the sun moves. Just as the gospel is true, geocentricity is true. The subject matter is not a spinning earth. Just as the gospel has gone around the earth, so also does the sun.

Psalm 74:17 says, "Thou hast set all the borders of the earth." God didn't set the "borders of the "sun, moon and stars" (universe). (The context is the universe, from verse 16). "Borders" cannot be crossed. God set them to keep things inside. If the border were around the "sun, moon and stars" then the earth could revolve around the sun inside the border of the universe, but it isn't. The earth cannot move through the borders set by the Lord, so the earth does not revolve around the sun yearly.

"The evidence for heliocentrism is even weaker than the evidence for evolution," wrote Dr. Jim Paulson, Professor of Biochemistry at the University of Wisconsin-Oshkosh. (Quoted in *The Biblical Astronomer*, Spring 2002, p. 80.)

Chapter 5

THE DENSITY AND CENTER
OF THE UNIVERSE

Dr. Robert J. Moon, physicist, University of Chicago, who is not a geocentricist, wrote on page 26 of *21st Century*, May 1988, saying, "free space is not a vacuum, but exhibits impedance, which equals 376+ ohms." So space (or the firmament) has a structure. According to accepted theory, free space is a vacuum. If this is so, how can it exhibit impedance (resistance)? But it does. The answer is that there is no such thing as a vacuum, and what we call free space actually has a structure.

The weight of the universe is next to nothing compared to the weight of the firmament. The size of the atom is about 10^{-13} cm. The size of the nucleus of the atom is about a thousandth of that or 10^{-16} cm. The size of the Planck particle is about 10^{-33} cm or billions of times smaller.

Isaiah 34:11 says, "...the stones of emptiness". Compared to Planck particles, the atom is empty. Isaiah 24:1 – "Behold, the Lord maketh the earth empty." The earth, made up of atoms, is basically empty compared to the firmament, which is made up of Planck particles. Both verses, previously considered figurative, now become literal. Plank particles are virtually invisible in the heaven or firmament, "in heaven and in earth, visible and invisible" (Colossians 1:16), a fact already known in scripture.

Normally the earth or stars would be thought to show His handiwork, but the density of the universe is next to nothing compared to the firmament, so the "firmament shows his handiwork" (Psalm 19:1).

The density in the nucleus of an atom is 2×10^{14} gm/cm^3 (a centimeter is about 3/8 inch). The density of a Planck particle is 3.6×10^{33} gm/cm^3 or many trillions of trillions times more compact. Packing everything in the universe (earth, planets and stars) into a one centimeter cube would only give a density of 2×10^{54} gm/cm^3 or 2×10^{39} times <u>less</u> than a cube of Planck particles which make up the firmament. "I will make your heaven (firmament) as iron" (Leviticus 26:19). This would seem to make the firmament immovable. Other verses supporting this are: "And the likeness of the firmament was... as the colour of the terrible crystal..." (Ezekiel 1:22). "And before the throne there was a sea of glass like unto crystal..." (Revelation 4:6). Glass and crystal are certainly hard and solid like **iron**.

ATOM	Planck particles
(electron)	00000
	00000
(proton)	00000

So far, we have a solid firmament, but it is also clear. "And they saw the God of Israel: and there was under his feet as it were a paved work of a sapphire stone, and as it were the body of heaven (firmament) in *his* clearness" (Exodus 24:10). From our viewpoint, the sky or heaven is clear, just empty space. Conversely, "the heavens are not clean in his sight" (Job 15:15). Webster's dictionary says "clean" means free from radioactivity. The firmament is not clean, but packed full of atomic structure (radioactivity) in the heavens. Is there any support for this theory? "And I saw as it were a sea of glass mingled with fire...(Rev 15:2). The word "fire" is referring to electromagnetism that is in the firmament. Job 37:18 continues: "the sky, which is strong, and as a molten looking glass?" The dictionary says "molten" means melting or liquefied by heat or fire. God is omnipotent, infinite, and omnipresent. One cannot cut a region of space so small that God's power therein is not infinite. Hence, God is a plenum, which means – all space every part of which is full of matter. "Do not I fill heaven and earth?" (Jeremiah 23:24) This is an understatement. So, the firmament is totally clear so you can see through it, yet is extremely dense with atomic structure including electromagnetism. The problems of mankind begin with a lack of understanding of the firmament. No wonder God didn't call the second day of creation, <u>good</u>, when the firmament was created!

CENTER

Is it possible to know where the center of the universe is and to know what is there? God's word tells us, but we must trust him and his scripture enough to believe him through his word.

"For behold, I create new heavens and a new earth" (Isaiah 65:17). The following verses tell how this is done. The earth will be present in the new heavens in some form, "...the earth which he hath established for ever." (Psa 78:69). As the present earth was cleansed by water and not destroyed, it will be cleansed by fire and again not destroyed. The cleansing will melt the elements making up the firmament. Peter 3:12, "...wherein the heavens being on fire shall be dissolved, and the elements shall melt with fervent heat?" The elements, which are located in the firmament or first heaven, including the sun, moon and stars, all melt and fall to the earth, melting it "...the earth melted" (Psalm 46:6). The present earth will then become the new earth, which is covered by the elements that were in the firmament.

Mark 13:8 – "...and there shall be earthquakes in divers places...these are the beginnings of sorrows." An earthquake is a sign of the beginning of sorrows or birth pangs. A baby is born right where the mother is, not on the other side of town. The new earth will also be restored right where the present earth is located, not a million miles away; again showing that the present earth is in the exact center of the universe. Rom 8:22 – "the whole creation groaneth and travaileth" awaiting the birth of the new earth. Duet. 4:11 says, "...and the mountain burned with fire unto the midst of heaven..." The fire burning to the middle of heaven shows that the earth is in the middle of heaven, firmament or universe, and not spinning in a corner, orbiting the sun.

Certainly the new earth will be in the center of the new heavens. Since the new earth will be where the present earth is, the present earth is in the center of the universe, firmament and heaven. The location is the same as it is now!

Backing this up is Ezek 5:5 which says, "Thus saith the Lord God; This is Jerusalem: I have set it in the midst of the nations and countries that are round about her." A computer study determined that the sum of the distances from Jerusalem to all other increments of land areas on the earth would be smaller than from any other point on the earth's surface. The people of Israel "dwell in the midst of the land" (Ezek 38:12); or the "center of the earth" and the earth is in the center of the universe.

The final solution must be going back to the absolute truth in the King James Bible, which is openly geocentric. R.G. Elmendorf wrote in the Biblical Astronomer pamphlet, "The philosophical consequences of the geocentric/heliocentric controversy are plain enough that if the earth is not fixed on center stage of the universe, then life on earth and man himself are essentially meaningless."

Chapter 6

PRESERVED

This is sent to the same group that received the "Geocentricity" book and my articles (*Geocentric Bible 1*). When I found out about the subject of the preservation of God's word in the King James Bible from the leaders of the geocentric movement, I thought, "UH HO, what next?" I write this article with a sense of embarrassment. The *New International Version* and *New American Standard Version* and other modern version are used through out our brotherhood and in our homes and great numbers of people have been led to Christ through them. After studying several books on this subject, it looks like there is a need to summarize this material. One good thing about this is that I do tremble at His word (Isaiah 66:2) to a greater extent.

Criticism is welcome.

The difference between Christ and Satan can appear to be very thin. Christ is the "bright and morning star." (Rev. 22:16). Satan is called the "son of the morning" (Isaiah 14:12). As both refer to the sun, Satan can be mistaken for Christ!

The majority viewpoint is to defend the inaccuracies in modern versions by stating: "Let's stick to where our Bibles agree rather than quarrel over where the disagree. Since so much of any modern translation is accurate and only a small portion is inaccurate, there is no cause for alarm." But we couldn't say that since I'm 98% healthy, I can ignore a cancer.

In 1869, someone writing in the *Gospel Standard,* said, "If the new translation were once to begin, where would it end? We should have a Bible that nobody would accept as the Word of God, to which none could safely appeal, and on which none implicitly rely. Modern versions breed confusion, doubt and misunderstanding."

"Beloved, believe not every spirit (version), but try the spirits whether they be of God..." (1 John 4:1). God expects us to examine modern versions of the Bible. When we do, "...the Spirit of truth...will guide you into all truth..." (John 16:13). The Holy

Spirit will identify the correct version, which is the KJV. Every verse has its mate to confirm any doctrine and this one does also, "Even the Spirit of truth...shall be in you" (John 14:17) showing new versions in their true light.

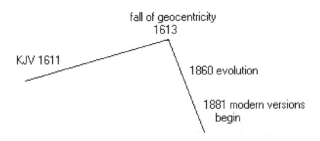

The fall of geocentricity and the beginning of the false theory of heliocentrism (the earth spinning daily) beginning in 1613 marked the division between the one perfect Bible, the KJV 1611 and the many corrupt versions. The false theory of evolution came in 1860, followed by the first corrupt modern version in 1881.

As the world was being offered an entirely new science, the Church was being furnished an entirely new Bible. After centuries of fruitful faith in the Bible, Christians began to doubt that they really had the Word of God. A generation was tricked into thinking that the defense of the "originals" was better than claiming to have the authoritative Word of God in their hands. WHY? The simple mistake in the 16th century of abandoning geocentricity (sun going around a stationary earth) and accepting heliocentrism (earth spinning and going around the sun). There is no proof for or against either theory; except God's word, but it falsely showed the Bible to be in error. "I have written to him the great things of my law, but they were counted as a strange thing" (Hosea 8:12). The scientific law of geocentricity was labeled as an error and cast aside.

DOCTRINE CHANGING

All modern versions attack, at least once, the major doctrines of the Bible, such as the deity of Christ, the virgin birth, etc.

Psalm 12:7 in the KJV says, "thou shalt keep them (the words of God)" "Them" refers to God's word that He has said He will preserve for ever. Psalm 12:7 in the NIV says "you will keep us" which eliminates the Bibles reference on Divine preservation. Obviously, the NIV, RSV, ASV and many others, which deny and confuse the deity of Christ, are not pure.

KJV John 6:47 "Verily, verily, I say unto you, He that believeth on me hath everlasting life." The New American Standard says, "Truly, truly, I say to you, he who believes has eternal life." He who believes on who or what?

KJV Hebrews 2:11, "For both he that sanctifieth and they who are sanctified are all of one: for which cause he is not ashamed to call them brethren." Revised Version of Hebrews 2:11 says, "For he who sanctifies and those who are sanctified have all one origin. That is why he is not ashamed to call them brethren." Christ did not have an origin. Psalm 90:2 says, "even from everlasting to everlasting thou art God." By saying that Christ had the same origin as man, they are saying that Christ is a created being.

Acts 3:26 says, "Unto you first God, having raised up his Son Jesus, sent him to bless you, in turning away every one of you from his iniquities. Acts 3:26, NKJV says, "Unto you first God, having raised up his servant Jesus, sent him to bless you, in turning away every one of you from your iniquities." Christ is God, not a mere "servant." Jeremiah 26:2 says "...diminish not a word."

Hebrews 2:11 in the KJV says "For both he that sanctifieth and they who are sanctified are all of one: for which cause he is not ashamed to call them brethren." The Revised Standard Version has "For he who sanctifies and those who are sanctified have all one origin. That is why he is not ashamed to call them brethren." The RSV adds "origin. Christ did not have an origin! Psalm 90:2 says, "even from everlasting to everlasting thou art God." By saying that Christ had the same origin as man, they are saying that Christ is a created being. That Christ is not God!

In the KJV, John 6:47 says, "Verily, verily, I say unto you, He that believeth on me hath everlasting life." The New American Standard has, "Truly, truly, I say to you, he who believes has eternal life." The NIV has, "I tell you the truth, he who believes has everlasting life." Both the NAS and NIV do not say what to believe in.

In the KJV, Isaiah 14:12 has "O Lucifer, son of the morning" one of the names of Satan, who was first created as an angel during creation week. By taking "Lucifer" out of The Ryrie Study Bible (New American Standard Translation), the reader would not know of Satan's beginning in the Bible. Also, the NAST has references listed, 2 Peter 1:19, Rev. 2:28 and 22:16; but these are to Jesus Christ, who is "the morning star." Christ cannot be connected in any way with this passage! The phrase, "son of the morning" and "the morning star" are totally and completely different.

The only verse in the New Testament, after the cross, that records the minister in the act of sharing the Gospel and a sinner's confession of faith in Christ is Acts 8:37. The reader of the NIV is eternally denied this verse.

Some people may read Matthew 9:13 in the NIV where the words "to repentance" are omitted and not compare it with Luke 5:32 where the words are not omitted. To justify an omission because it can be found somewhere else fails when tested by scripture, "a little leaven leaveneth the whole lump" (1 Cor. 5:6).

In the KJV Micah 5:2 says, "out of thee shall he come forth unto me that is to be ruler in Israel; whose goings forth have been from of old, from everlasting." The NIV says, "out of you will come for me one who will be ruler over Israel, whose origins are from old, from ancient times." According to this, Christ was not eternal.

In the KJV, Matt. 9:18 says, "there came a certain ruler, and worshipped him." The NIV has, "a ruler came and knelt before him" You can bow respectfully before royalty without worship.

In the KJV, Matt. 5:22 says, "...whosoever is angry with his brother without a cause..." The NIV says, "whosoever is angry with his brother." The NIV would have Christ breaking his own command and would then not be sinless.

Since all modern versions eliminate themselves, the only one left is the KJV. The KJV has "many infallible proofs" because it is the only one that does not deny and confuse the deity of Christ. Mat 7:20 says, "Wherefore by their fruits ye shall know them." We know the modern versions are wrong because of the doubt they are producing.

The Holy Spirit could not possibly have guided the writers of modern versions to write these verses. Only one verse that diminishes the deity of Christ is enough for us to realize that the Holy Spirit had nothing to do with that entire version, because God is perfect. In modern versions, a verse is wrong in one place and right in another. A busy family man with a job may look at the wrong verse and never realize that the verse is right in another location. Let's recall that just one "error," that the KJV is geocentric, started all modern versions.

The NIV has shown its true colors by wanting to make a new version gender free. Let's use modern versions only as a paraphrase, not as the word of God. In the beginning the greatest attacks on the Bible came from enemies. Now, attacks come from within, by Christians who doubt the word of God.

I Timothy 3:16, KJV says, "And without controversy great is the mystery of godliness: God was manifest in the flesh..." This verse clearly teaches that Jesus is God, because Jesus is the one who came in the flesh. Therefore, <u>Jesus is God</u>! The New American Standard has, "And by common confession great is the mystery of godliness: He who was revealed in the flesh..." By changing "God" to "He," the fact that Jesus is God is taken out! The Living Bible has, "It is quite true that the way to live godly life is not an easy matter..." "It is quite true" is the <u>opposite</u> of "without controversy."

"Hold fast the <u>form</u> of sound words" (2 Timothy 1:13). Form means "a prescribed and set order of words" or a "formula." A formula cannot be changed and have the same solution. By changing words, modern versions diminish and deny the deity of Christ, plus destroy cross-references.

When God is aware of such ordinary things as: [is there any taste in the white of an egg? (Job 6:6)], He must have been aware of the coming of corrupt versions. Also, He declared "the end from the beginning" (Isaiah 46:10).

Modern versions do "word studies" which dig downward to a dead-end which may or may not be correct.

Change is not always progress: "and meddle not with them that are given to change" (Proverbs 24:21).

NO DOCTRINE IS CHANGED

The King James Bible is the 7th major translation in the English language: 1st the Wycliffe Bible - 1382, 2nd - Tyndale Bible - 1525, 3rd - Matthews Bible, 4th - The Great Bible - 1539, 5th - Geneva - 1560, 6th - the Bishop Bible – 1568 and 7th - the King James Bible. Psalms 12:6 says, "The words of the Lord are pure words: as silver tried in a furnace of earth, purified seven times." Only the words of the King James has been purified 7 times. None of these diminished the deity of Christ. The Holy Spirit inspired only the KJV. How do we know for sure that this is true? It never once attacks or diminishes or confuses the doctrine of the deity of Christ. In the KJV, any word added to make a verse more readable, was put in italics. At the very least, this is more honest than modern versions. In all other versions, there are no italics, whole verses have been chopped out and major doctrines have been reversed.

Acts 7:38 "...the lively oracles to give unto us." The footnote says this means: the living words, the words of God. God has given his living words to us. Ephesians 3:16 "...be strengthened with the might by his Spirit in the inner man." Phil 2:5 "Let this mind be in you, which was also in Christ Jesus." Proverbs 1:23 says, "...I will pour out my spirit unto you, I will make known my words unto you." Therefore, we have his Spirit, his mind and his promise to "make known my words" to us. This has to be the King James Version.

"For he received from God the Father honour and glory, when there came such a voice to him from the excellent glory..." (2 Peter 1:17). The written word is more sure than <u>God speaking from heaven.</u> Peter, James and John had been on the mount when the transfiguration of Christ took place, "...when we were with him in the holy mount. We have a more sure word of prophecy...," (vs. 18,19). Peter refers to scripture as being a more sure word of prophecy than the transfiguration that took place before his eyes. How could this be? Continuing with verse 19, "... whereunto ye do well that ye take heed...until the day dawn, and the day star arise in your hearts." We need to (take heed) pay particular attention that the day dawns only because the sun rises. As the day-star, Christ, rises in our hearts, so the sun (a type of Christ) rises. If we change our belief to geocentricity then we will have a more sure word of prophecy than seeing the transfiguration! During the transfiguration 'his face did shine as the sun" (Matt.17:2). Imagine the brightness from the sun if we were 40 feet away from it (assuming there was no heat). No darkness would be possible. The scripture is more sure than God's voice and God's light. The King James Bible IS the inspired and preserved Word of God; just the way the Lord wants to have it. All the words that were in the original autographs are in the King James Bible. This will make our faith in Christ even more secure.

VAIN

"Do ye think that the scripture saith in vain...?" (James 4:5). Jeremiah 8:8 "...the pen of the scribes is in vain." Since the scribes write scripture, is the scripture written in vain or not? The KJV is correct, and the writing of modern versions will eventually be cast away. It is impossible for anything that God does to be in vain, "...I am the LORD, and that I have not said in vain" (Ezek 6:10).

The first apostasy took place in heaven, in the presence of God when Lucifer turned angels against Him. After Pentecost the church at Pergamos could have the doctrine of Balaam, but they chose not to. With this in mind, corrupted scriptures could easily have penetrated the Church, but they didn't. Then, because the Bible was challenged with scientific "errors," modern translations were written, which are as traitorous to the "written word" (98% perfect is not good enough) as Judas was to the "living word."

ORIGINALS

It would do no good to inspire the "originals" and then lose them. Peter, John etc. had a perfect Bible plus they were with Christ. We need a perfect Bible even more because we haven't seen or heard the Lord. "Howbeit when he, the Spirit of truth, is come, he will guide you into all truth..." (John 16:13). This was only partly fulfilled on the day of Pentecost.

"I (the Lord) will put my laws into their mind, and write them in their hearts" (Heb 8:10). "For the ear trieth words, as the mouth tasteth meat." (Job 34:3). God has said that he has given us the truth, so we must know which version is correct in order to fully believe him.

"All the words of my mouth are in righteousness; there is nothing froward or perverse in them. They are all plain to him that understandeth, and right to them that find knowledge" (Prov. 8:8,9). Scripture becomes plain when we understand that the Bible is geocentric and scripture has been preserved.

The original manuscripts of the Bible were destroyed by fire in Jeremiah 36:21-32. But instead of being destroyed, the original record was expanded! "...And there were added besides unto them many like words" (Jeremiah 36:32). If God wasn't interested in preserving the "original" once it had been copied and its message delivered, why should we put more emphasis on the original than God does. God wrote His word on the hearts of believers, and Christ sent the Holy Spirit when he left. The Holy Spirit did not work 200-300 years and quit, but is continuing to guide us. With the Holy Spirits guidance into all truth, we can know that modern versions are wrong and useful only as a paraphrase.

"And the temple of God was opened in heaven, and there was seen in his temple the ark of his testament..." Rev 11:19. The "originals" were destroyed, but God's "original" is probably kept in the heavenly Ark of the Covenant for eternal reference.

The word "scripture" in 2 Timothy 3:16, is in the context of verse 15, which says "scriptures" not "original" manuscripts.

INSPIRATION

"But there is a spirit in man: and the inspiration of the Almighty giveth them understanding." (Job 32:8). "All scripture is given by inspiration of God, and is profitable for doctrine, for reproof, for correction, for instruction in righteousness:" (2 Tim 3:16). We all agree that the Bible is inspired by the Lord.

Inspiration means an act of breathing in. In 2 Kings 18:13-19:37 is the story of Hezekiah and Isaiah trusting God to deliver them from Senacherib. The same story is in Isaiah 37-38 with the additional information of Hezekiah's sickness and recovery. The work of inspiration in the giving of scripture took place twice. The second inspired writing was superior to the first even though it did not match the first. "When Moses came down from Mt. Sinai he had "two tables of testimony, tables of stone, written with the finger of God" (Exodus 31:18). Exodus 34:1 says, "And the Lord said unto Moses, Hew thee two tables of stone like unto the first: and I will write upon these tables the words that were in the first tables, which thou brakest." Hebrews 9:4 says, "Which had...the ark of the covenant...wherein was...the tables of the covenant." The second inspiration became the authority and was superior to the first.

When the Scriptures refer to the "scriptures" they never refer to the originals." Inspiration applies not only to the "originals" but also to copies and translations. All of the Old Testament quotations in the New Testament show the inspiration of a translation, since they are translated from Hebrew into Greek.

The word "inspiration" occurs in 2 Timothy 3:16. There must be a "mate" verse to support and explain in the verse we are working with. The word "inspire" is not in the Bible. The only other time the word "inspiration" occurs the in the Bible is Job 32:8 and here it is not dealing with scripture! Verse 8 says, "But there is a spirit in man: and the inspiration of the Almighty giveth them understanding." God "breathed in" to only one man: Adam. Yet the inspiration of the Almighty is applied to "them," to all men not just Adam. God breathed into Adam and it applied to all 6 billion of us. "The spirit of God hath made me, and the breath of the Almighty hath given me life" (Job 33:4), which supports Job 32:8.

The two verses are connected; but how? One is dealing with scripture and the other with men! The Almighty God is telling us that the miracle of inspiration applies not only to the initial giving of the Word of God to the writers of the original autographs, but to the divinely superintended preservation of a pure text to this day. The King James Bible is an inspired translation of the "original autographs." The King James Bible is those same autographs preserved up to today.

OUR SOULS PRESERVED

Preservation is very valuable and necessary for our own souls. We absolutely want preservation to have true meaning in the following verses.

1 Thessalonians 5:23 says, "...and I pray God your whole spirit and soul and body be preserved blameless unto the coming of

our Lord Jesus Christ."

Matt. 9:17,"...but they put new wine into new bottles, and both are preserved."

1 Thess. 5:23,"...your whole spirit and body and soul be preserved blameless..."

Jude 1,"...to them that are sanctified by God the Father, and preserved in Jesus Christ..."

Psalm 121:7,8 "...He shall preserve thy soul..."

GOD'S WORD PRESERVED

The word, preserved, must continue to mean the same thing. "The words of the LORD are pure words: as silver tried in a furnace of earth, purified seven times. Thou shalt keep them, O LORD, thou shalt preserve them from this generation for ever." (Psalm 12:6,7). God used sinful men to write His inspired words and God used sinful men to preserve His words. Psalm 119:89 says, "For ever, O LORD, thy word is settled in heaven."

THE PROGRESSION IS UPWARD

Adam and Eve heard the actual voice of God.

Moses heard the voice and saw the handwriting of God

The disciples, being with Jesus, had the absolute truth.

The more time, the more we know about God.

Christ was in one location at one time, but now, we have the Holy Spirit who is everywhere, all of the time and Bibles are throughout the world. Everyone should know the truth that God wants us to have, completely at any time.

INSTEAD we don't know, even in Gen.1:2, whether the Spirit moved (KJV) or didn't move (modern versions; only hovered - NIV). We are entitled to the same absolute truth that people had up to the 17th century. If God wrote or dictated verses that we can't use them till we get to heaven, then he has wasted his time putting them in the Bible. If we don't know what verses mean till we get to heaven, it will be too late to use them.

"And he wrote on the tables, according to the first writing, the Ten Commandments, which the LORD spake unto you..." (Deuteronomy 10:4). Moses had the stone tablets written with the actual handwriting of God. The prophets had the truth. The disciples and other people, who were with Jesus, face to face, had absolute truth. So far, everyone knew what God meant. Every word was established. We are entitled to the same, but instead, we have to pick and choose verses from a dozen different versions to get the truth!? The truth is that we have God's will in written form just as Moses did. If we have to choose which version is correct, when they say the opposite things, then we are God instead of the Lord. "For God is not the author of confusion..." (1 Cor. 14:33).

"But the word of the Lord endureth for ever..."(1 Pet. 1:25). In Joshua 6, when God gave instructions concerning the wall of Jericho, He did not promise he would make the walls fall, but he did. God promised to "preserve his word" so we can absolutely count on its being preserved.

He preserved the Old Testament through the Levites as priest and He has preserved the New Testament through the body of believers and through the witness of the Holy Spirit.

INTERPRET

Let's let God and His scripture do the interpreting. "Do not interpretations belong to God?" (Gen 40:8). Joseph depended on God for the correct interpretation, "that thou canst understand a dream to interpret it. It is not in me: God shall give...an answer..." (Gen 41:15,16). Recorded in 2 Peter 1:20 is the basic principals of interpretation, "...no prophecy of the scripture is of any private interpretation." Every verse is explained and made complete by another verse, Isaiah 34:16, "...none (no verse) shall want her mate..." 1 Cor. 2:13 supports this doctrine, "Which things also we speak, not in the words which man's wisdom teacheth, but which the Holy Ghost teacheth; comparing spiritual things with spiritual." Always, one verse gives a statement and another verse gives the answer and explanation necessary.

To summarize, God has inspired, preserved, and interpreted scripture. Just as there is "...one body..." (1 Cor 12:12) one mediator (1 Tim. 2:5) "One Lord, one faith, one baptism..." (Eph 4:5), there is also only one doctrine. From the dictionary "faith" is the belief in the doctrines expressed in scripture. The word "doctrines" is always used in a negative sense in scripture. There is only one "doctrine of Christ: (2 John 9).

TRANSLATION

The conversations between Moses and Pharaoh, in Egyptian, were translated into the "original autographs" which were in Hebrew. God chose the Hebrew language that less than 1% of the world ever spoke, to write $3/4^{ths}$ of everything He wanted said. Translations <u>have</u> to be inspired.

"And he believed in the LORD..." (Gen 15:6). "For what saith the scripture? Abraham believed God..." (Rom 4:3). Paul wrote both New Testament verses in Greek when he quotes the Old Testament, which is written in Hebrew. This means that a translation can be inspired.

Old Testament "original" manuscripts were written is Hebrew. New Testament "original" manuscripts were written is Greek. Matthew 8:17 (in Greek) is a translation of Isaiah 53:4 (Hebrew). Matthew 11:10 (Christ speaking) is a translation of Isaiah 40:3. Romans11:8 is a translation of Isaiah 29:10. The scribes did not have the first copy that Moses wrote. They had the scriptures! Timothy did not have David's original autograph of Psalm 2, but the scripture. There are over 50 translations in the New Testament of Old Testament Hebrew passages.

Exodus 7:11 reads, "Then Pharaoh also called the wise men and the sorcerers: now the magicians of Egypt..." The names of the two magicians, Jannes and Jambres, is listed only in 2 Timothy 3:8. Also in 1 Kings 17:1 which says, "...there shall not be dew nor rain these years, but according to my word", the length of the drought, three years and six months, is found in Luke 4:25 and James 5:17. God, himself, chose to preserve these facts, written in Hebrew, for centuries, and then complete them in Greek. The Lord is showing that copies of scripture can be preserved and that a translation in English can be inspired and more complete than the original manuscripts. The church that "kept my word" (Rev. 3:8) was the Philadelphia church (1500-1800), not the early Apostolic church.

The word "scripture" is always used of copies or translations and does not refer to "original autographs." In Luke 4:21, Christ read the Old Testament scripture of Isaiah 61:1, 2, which was a copy of a copy of copies. He had no "original" of Isaiah. He accepted the scripture that He had as the absolute truth. Christ rebuked people for not reading the scripture (Matt. 22:29), so they had to have the right scripture. Christ would not encourage the reading anything false, nor demanding them to read something that wasn't available. The Ethiopian eunuch had the scripture (Acts 8:28) open on his lap in the church dispensation! We have to have it.

The Authorized Version 1611 says, "And the nations of them which are saved shall walk in the light of it..." (Rev. 21:24). The New American Standard says, "And the nations shall walk by its light..." leaving out "of them which are saved." All nations are obviously not saved, "And before him shall be gathered all nations: and he shall separate them one from another, as a shepherd divideth his sheep from the goats" (Matthew 25:32). All modern versions come from corrupt Greek manuscripts. The King James English corrects the Greek.

INTERCHANGEABLY

"For the scripture saith unto Pharaoh, Even for this same purpose have I raised thee up, that I might shew my power in thee, and that my name might be declared throughout all the earth" (Rom. 9:17). This verse is quoting Exodus 9:16, in which God himself personally said, "And in very deed for this cause have I raised thee up, for to shew in thee my power; and that my name may be declared throughout all the earth." This means that "Scripture saith" is synonymous with "God saith." They can be used interchangeably. Another example of the same thing is: "Therefore thus saith the Lord GOD, Behold, I lay in Zion for a foundation a stone, a tried stone, a precious corner stone, a sure foundation: he that believeth shall not make haste" (Isaiah 28:16). "Wherefore also it is contained in the scripture, Behold, I lay in Sion a chief corner stone, elect, precious: and he that believeth on him shall not be confounded" (1 Pet 2:6). What God says and what is contained in scripture are the same and equally true. All the trustworthiness of God Himself rests upon the written Word of scripture. "But I will show thee that which is noted in the scripture of truth...." (Daniel 10:21). God's written word is the scripture of truth.

Jesus Christ, who wrote with His finger, "Honor thy father and thy mother" (Exodus 20:10), personally ascribed the authorship of the passage to Moses in Mark 7:10, "For Moses said, Honour thy father and thy mother..." That which Moses had copied from the stone tablet, was fully the word of God. There was no difference to Christ.

1 Peter 1:25 says, "But the word of the Lord endureth for ever. And this is the word which by the gospel is preached unto you." The word of the Lord, scripture, is God. After all, the Holy Spirit is the author: "Which he had promised afore by his prophets in the holy scriptures." (Romans 1:2). Only the Holy Spirit knew the promises from Genesis to Malachi.

FORESEEING

"And in thy seed shall all the nations of the earth be blessed..." (Genesis 22:18). This is referred to in Galatians 3:8, "And the scripture, foreseeing that God...preached before the gospel unto Abraham, saying, In thee shall all nations be blessed" How could scripture foresee anything? The only one that can foresee anything is the Holy Spirit. Therefore, scripture is equal with the Holy Spirit. Also, scripture couldn't have preached anything to Abraham, because there were no scriptures written then. Moses did not write Genesis 22 until 400 years after God said through Abraham all nations be blessed. The Holy Spirit is the only one that could have preached! But it says, scripture...preached. So, again, scripture is the same as the Holy Spirit.

When the LIVING WORD (Christ) returned to glory, Satan turned all of his fury upon the WRITTEN WORD. The living word had "many infallible proofs" Acts 1:3. The Holy Spirit guided the written word. Since the Holy Spirit is equal with Christ, the "Written Word" is just as infallible as the "Living Word"!

But the written word is living just as much as Christ, "...by the word of God, which liveth and abideth for ever" (1 Peter 1:23). And how is scripture living? It is living because God has written it on our hearts and minds, "...saith the Lord; I will put my laws into their mind, and write them in their hearts..." (Hebrews 8:10). Jeremiah 31:33 also says, "...and write it in their hearts..." We know in our heart and mind, with the Holy Spirit's leading, when a version is wrong. God's truth in <u>living</u> scripture will not allow changes to doctrine. "Let not...truth forsake thee...write them upon the table of thine heart" (Proverbs 3:3). "But the Scripture hath concluded" (Galatians 3:22). "Conclude" means reach a decision by reasoning. There is a sense in which scripture can reason as God can.

COMFORTER

John 16:7 says, "Nevertheless I tell you the truth; It is expedient for you that I go away: for if I go not away, the Comforter will not come unto you; but if I depart, I will send him unto you." Christ said that the Comforter, the Holy Spirit, would give us help that we needed very much, "Howbeit when he, the Spirit of truth, is come, he will guide you into <u>all</u> truth," (John 16:13). Psalm 100:5 says, "and his truth endureth to all generations." Every generation has the complete total truth as reveled in the King James Version, just as the disciples did when talking directly with Jesus.

When Christ left, the Holy Spirit, the Comforter, came. "It is better to trust in the Lord than to put confidence in men" (Psalm 118:8). This verse is the very center verse of the Bible. The shortest chapter in the Bible is Psalm 117 and the longest chapter is Psalm 119. The phrase "long and short of it" means "the overall point" or the "basic idea." Putting it all together, the point God is stressing is to trust his words rather than what men think regardless of whether we totality understand it or not.

Christ "taught them as one having authority" (Mark 1:22). He taught face to face. The Holy Spirit took the place of Christ and should be teaching with the same authority as Christ; "But the Comforter, which is the Holy Ghost, whom the Father will send in my name, he shall teach you all things, and bring all things to your remembrance, whatsoever I have said unto you"(John 14:26). The Holy Spirit, being the author of scripture teaches through scripture instead of in person as Christ did. But, we should still have the absolute truth just as the disciples did!

However, because of modern versions, we do not know whether the Spirit moved or not in Genesis 1:2! Regardless of manuscripts, translations or anything else, the Holy Spirit has delivered the exact absolute truth to us in the King James Bible.

Jesus told the disciples the age and size of the universe and how it operates. Likewise, the Holy Spirit has told us that the earth is young, that the sun orbits the earth (geocentricity), the ballpark size of the universe and that scripture has been preserved. "All the words of my mouth are in righteousness; there is nothing froward or perverse in them. They are all plain to him that understandeth, and right to them that find knowledge." (Proverbs 8:8,9). All of God's words become plain if we trust the Lord enough to believe him, when he said that he would preserve his words in the King James scripture.

Heb. 13:5 says "...for he hath said, I will never leave thee, nor forsake thee." Had we been living when Christ was on the earth, we know that He would never leave us. It doesn't make sense that the Holy Spirit who "will guide you into all truth" (John 16:13) would leave us with the agonizing decision of deciding which word to choose. Those living in the past didn't have to guess what verses meant. We shouldn't have to guess either. Let's let scripture interpret scripture. Greek and Hebrew manuscripts can be made to say what a person wants them to say. God himself will not "alter the thing" or one word, (Psalm 89:34).

God's word was in the hearts of the writers of the Old and New Testaments; they knew when a doctrine was changed. Therefore, they didn't accept it. With our vantage point of being able to look back over the past, and with the living word in our hearts, we can "rightly divide" the written word and also be able to see the truth. So, all Bibles leading up to, and including the KJV, can have errors in spelling and minor word changes and still have God's complete Word, which is "written not with ink, but with the Spirit of the Living God; not in tables of stone, but in fleshy tables of the heart" (2 Cor. 3:3). Because the Holy Spirit writes on the hearts of Christians, we can understand which version is correct.

"Jesus Christ the same yesterday, and to day, and for ever" (Heb 13:8). But how about scripture? It shouldn't have changed either, because the Holy Spirit has control of it and is guiding us into "all truth" (John 16:13). Vs. 9 says, "Be not carried about with divers and strange doctrines. The "strange" doctrine of heliocentrism has changed scripture in the modern versions to the opposite meaning of the King James.

These verses show that there are inspired words of God that are not in scripture. "Ye likewise read the epistle from Laodicea" (Col 4:16). "And with many other words did he testify and exhort..." (Acts 2:40). "Is not this written in the book of Jasher?" (Joshua 10:13). "The book of Jasher, evidently, was like an astronomy book. Since the Bible is inspired, for scripture to mentioned the book of Jasher, means it must have been inspired also. This makes the scripture we do have, even more important, knowing we have exactly what God wants us to have.

Matt. 24:35 says, "...the scripture cannot be broken." It has by now been broken thousands of times with omissions and words changed and added. Can any changes be made now to the KJV? The standard meaning of "the word of God is not bound" (2 Tim 2:9) is that Paul is bound, but not the gospel.

When modern versions change words, they conceal the true meaning. "For I have not concealed the words of the Holy One (Job 6:10). "I will teach you be the hand of God: *that* which *is* with the Almighty will I not conceal" (Job 27:11).

THING

Luke 1:35 records "that holy thing which shall be born of thee shall be called the Son of God." Why is Christ is called a "thing?" "Thing" means a spoken or written observation. Scripture is also a book or a "thing." Calling Jesus Christ a "thing" makes scripture equal with Christ, and that is the point God is making. "It seemed good to me also, having had perfect understanding of all things from the very first..." (Luke 1:3). Luke and the disciples had perfect understanding of all "things" from the beginning. They understood Christ's creative work and all scripture from Genesis 1:1 forward.

A word of caution: (Now after all of the above?). I hesitate to write the following paragraph.

"Beloved, believe not every spirit, but try the spirits whether they are of God..." (1 John 4:1). The footnote says, No matter how holy men's teachings may appear to be, they must be tested by the Word of God. "And every spirit that confesseth not that Jesus Christ is come in the flesh is not of God: and this is that spirit of antichrist, whereof ye have heard that it should come; and even now already is it in the world" (1 John 4:3). The word "spirit" widens the base of who or what the antichrist may be. Modern versions are therefore included. There can also be a thin line between being for Christ and against Christ. The antichrist is not stopped by a mile wide demilitarized zone. The NIV and NASB have only "Christ" for 2 Cor. 5:18, instead of "Jesus Christ" as in the KJV. "They stripped him" (Matt. 27:28) of his divine titles, one step at a time. This is just one example, from page 303 of "New Age Bible Versions" by G. A. Riplinger, a book against modern versions. There are many versions just as there are "many antichrists" (1 John 2:18), which mix truth and falsehood.

"Satan himself is transformed into an angel of light" (2 Cor.11:14). However, "God is light" (1 John 1:5). Which of the two lights is God? Only with scripture, can we tell who is who.

EGYPT

The law of first mention says that the first time a subject is mentioned usually sets the light in which that subject shall reside in scripture. "When the Egyptians shall see thee, that they shall say, This is his wife: and they will kill me, but they will save thee (Sarai) alive" (Genesis 12:12). The first time Egypt in mentioned, it is in a negative air. Antioch is first mentioned in Acts 6:5 when Nicolas, a Christian from Antioch, was chosen as one of the first deacons. So, Antioch is mentioned is a positive light.

"But he shall not multiply horses to himself, nor cause the people to return to Egypt, to the end that he should multiply horses: forasmuch as the LORD hath said unto you, Ye shall henceforth return no more that way" (Deut 17:16). If God doesn't want His people to go down to Egypt for horses, we shouldn't go there for a Bible or an ideology. God also called His son (Hosea 2:15), the Israelites (Micah 6:4), Jacob out of Egypt (Gen. 49:30), "And the bones of Joseph...out of Egypt" (Josh 24:32). Neither can we get manuscripts out of Egypt, the very place where the corrupt manuscripts come from! Modern versions rely heavily on two corrupted manuscripts, Vaticanus and Siniaticus, which differ even from one another in over 3000 places in the gospels and have about 5000 omissions. [In Mark 14:56,59 the witnesses against Christ did not agree with each other either.] These two Alexandrian manuscripts are indebted for their preservation, solely to their ascertained evil character. One was found on a forgotten shelf in the Vatican library and the other in a waste-paper basket. God also "brought a vine out of Egypt" (Psalm 80:8).

The majority manuscripts, numbering in the thousands, and coming from Antioch, agree with each other. This should be the focus of attention in deciding which manuscripts to follow, instead of dates. Job 28:20 says, "Whence then cometh wisdom? and where is the place of understanding?" "Place" means location. The date that manuscripts are written is not important, but whether they are written in Antioch or Egypt. Isaiah 30:1 says, "Woe to the rebellious children saith the Lord, that take counsel, but not of me...and trust in the shadow of Egypt your confusion." When no two versions read the same way, no one knows what to believe.

(Jeremiah 2:36) "Why gaddest thou about so much to change thy way? thou also shalt be ashamed of Egypt..." This verse applies directly to the debate between the King James Bible and modern versions. The Lord knew far in advance that the church would want to change from the KJV to modern versions.

(Matthew 4:4) "But he answered and said, It is written, Man shall...live by...every word that proceedeth out of the mouth of God." How can God hold us responsible for every single word of the Bible and then confuse parts of the instructions? The true word of God has to be totally complete and on the earth, not just in heaven. "For ever O LORD, thy word is settled in heaven" (Psalm 119:89). If the perfect originals were locked up in heaven, they would be of no use to us now when we need them. But we do have them in the King James Bible.

We can pray direct to God, without going through a priest. We are "a royal priesthood" (1 Peter 2:9). Likewise, God can communicate directly with us. His written word does not have to go through scholars, but we do have to read and study, a word not found in most modern versions.

If God has included verses that are impossible for us to know the meaning of, until we get to heaven, then he has wasted his time putting them in the Bible. To the law and to the testimony: if they speak not according to this word, it is because there is no light in them (Isaiah 8:20). The Bible is overtly geocentric. If a modern version does not agree with this statement, it has no truth, regardless of how much knowledge it seems to have. "The law of the Lord is perfect, converting the soul: the testimony of the Lord is sure, making wise the simple." (Psalm 19:4a, 6,7). "In them (the heavens) hath he set a tabernacle for the sun...His going forth is from the end of the heaven, and his circuit unto the ends of it: and there is nothing hid from the heat thereof. Understanding how the universe operates is easy, if we accept God's answers. "To him that by wisdom made the heavens" (Psalm 136:5a). God made the heavens and firmament according to his wisdom, not ours.

LATTER OR LAST DAYS

Acts 2:17 says, "And it shall come to pass in the last days, saith God, I will pour out of my Spirit upon all flesh: and your sons and your daughters shall prophesy, and your young men shall see visions, and your old men shall dream dreams: And on my servants and on my handmaidens I will pour out in those days of my Spirit; and they shall prophesy:" This verse applies to the day of Pentecost. "And it shall come to pass afterward, that I will pour out my spirit" (Joel 2:28). The word "afterward" shows this verse applies to a later time than Pentecost, to the 1611 KJV. As always, this verse has a mate, "...I will pour out my spirit unto you, I will make known my words unto you" (Prov 1:23). God has made known his words to us through the KJV, that doesn't diminish or deny the deity of Christ. From our vantage point now, we can see that modern versions are useful only as paraphrases. "Knowing this first, that there shall come in the last days scoffers, walking after their own lusts" (2 Pet 3:3). Scoffing at the idea of a young earth, geocentricity, and the belief that there can be absolutes.

Will the saving gospel of Jesus Christ be spread through out the world before the end or not? Lets examine two verses. "And this gospel of the kingdom shall be preached in all the world for a witness unto all nations; and then shall the end come" (Matthew 24:14). "Behold, the days come, saith the Lord GOD, that I will send a famine in the land, not a famine of bread, nor a thirst for water, but of hearing the words of the LORD" (Amos 8:11). Are the words of the Lord, the gospel spread throughout the world or not? There are missionaries in every country preaching most of the Bible, but leaving out the subject of creation, geocentricity and preservation of scripture. This produces the famine of the very verses we desperately need to remove the idea that there can be errors in God's word.

NAME

"That at the name of Jesus every knee should bow, of things in heaven, and things in earth, and things under the earth;" (Phil 2:10). God's word, scripture, should be even more unchanging and true and total reality than his name is "for thou hast magnified thy <u>word</u> above all thy <u>name</u>" (Psalm 138:2). But this isn't the situation we find ourselves in. God's word, which is above his name, has not survived as well as his name. No one knows if his word exists or where it is located. Scripture is magnified above the name of Jesus Christ and should be as unchanging as Christ is! "Some trust in chariots, and some in horses: but we will remember the name of the LORD our God" (Psalm 20:7). God's name is better than an army.

(Joshua 3:7,9) "And the LORD said unto Joshua, This day will I begin to magnify thee in the sight of all Israel, that they may know that, as I was with Moses, so I will be with thee." "And Joshua said unto the children of Israel, Come hither, and hear the words of the LORD your God." Joshua began by declaring that they would hear the <u>actual</u> words of the Lord, not merely the words of Joshua.

WORD

Thessalonians 2:13 says, "the word of God which ye heard of us, ye received it not as the word of men, but as it is in truth, the word of God." Based on this, we must have God's word and it is the King James Bible, because it is the only one that does not deny or confuse the deity of Christ. The word "Word" in the New Testament always denotes speech or utterance, not reason or thought. "Thy words were found, and I did eat them; and thy word was unto me the joy and rejoicing of mine heart" (Jeremiah 15:16). By accepting modern versions, which have many ideas about what a verse means, the "word" is not a joy, but a strain, because people are trying to decide which version to use on a particular verse.

"What ye know, the same do I know also: I am not inferior unto you" (Job 13:2). Any Christian, with the KJB and study, can know as much as a church leader. The Lord must surely have known that modern versions were coming, to include this verse.

(John 14:23) "Jesus answered and said unto him, If a man love me, he will keep my <u>words</u>..." not the Word of God. We must have the words of God (KJV) or God is telling us to do something we could not do. "In the beginning was the Word, and the Word was with God, and the Word was God" (John 1:1). The Word is eternal and the words of God (Scripture) are also eternal. Scriptures are "the word of God" and contain "the words of God." "For he whom God hath sent speaketh the words of God (John 3:34). "...The words that I speak unto you, they are spirit, and they are life" (John 6:63). "For I have given unto them the words which thou gavest me..." (John 17:8). We have access to the actual and absolute words of God. In Luke 4:35 Jesus spoke 8 words and verse 36 says, "What a word is this! Eight words are called just one word. Jesus Christ told us to "Search the scriptures..." (John 5:39). At least, the Old Testament was available. He wouldn't have asked us to search Old Testament scriptures in modern versions that diminish or deny His deity. Timothy had to have the true scripture, "And that from a child thou hast known the holy scriptures..." (2 Tim 3:15). Timothy had the <u>absolute</u> truth from God right on his lap.

More proof? Proverbs 4:20,21 says, "My son, attend to my words; incline thine ear unto my sayings. Let them not depart from thine eyes..." We can see the words God wants us to have. We can <u>see</u> the actual words from God, not message, but words. We are "face to face" with the words. Jesus basically quoted Proverbs 4:19 in John 12:35. The next verse (v. 36) says, "...These things spake Jesus, and departed, and did hide himself from them." Jesus, who is the Word, departed because "they believed not on him" (v. 37). They didn't believe the words He spoke. We do not want the "words" (Proverbs 4:21) to depart from us because of unbelief.

In the dictionary the word, "word" means communication and words can be either spoken or written. Our Lord Jesus Christ was the Word (John 1:1) and "the Word was made flesh" (John 1:14).

232

Why is Jesus Christ called the "Word?" To emphasize that "word of truth" (2 Timothy 2:15) and "scripture of truth" (Daniel 10:21) are identical. Hebrews 13:5 says, "For he (Jesus) hath said, I will never leave thee, nor forsake thee."

Before the crucifixion Jesus prayed that God's word (John 17:6) and "the words which thou gavest me" (v. 8) would be kept by as many "as thou hast given me" (v. 9). So when Jesus went back to heaven after the resurrection, what happened to the Word? It is preserved in scripture. How? By the Holy Spirit inspiring men. Jesus did not mind leaving, because he knew that his replacement, the Holy Spirit, would "guide you into all truth" (John 16:13). Since the Holy Spirit and Jesus are equal and always agree "and these three agree in one" (1 John 5:8), the Holy Spirit has preserved the "word of truth" (Ephesians 1:13) with the written "scripture of truth" (Daniel 10:21) just as Christ spoke with his disciples "face to face." The King James scripture is just as reliable and accurate as Jesus talking to us.

"I will...praise thy name...for thy truth: for thou hast magnified thy word above all thy name" (Psalm 138:2). The name of God includes all the perfections of God; everything that God is, and which God has revealed Himself as having. He has magnified His written word, which is written in the sacred scripture above all His Name! His Name stands for Himself. He would suffer the loss of Himself, if possible, rather than let His words in scripture fail. "He that rejecteth me, and receiveth not my words, hath one that judgeth him: the word that I have spoken, the same shall judge him in the last day" (1 John 12:48). His word, which contains his words, will judge us. We have to have the exact words. We cannot be judged over information we do not have. "In the mouth of two or three witnesses shall every word be established" (2 Cor. 13:1). Every word needs to be positively known in a court case between men. This is all the more reason for us to absolutely know every word of scripture. There cannot be any doubt at all about any word.

1 John 3:3 says, "And every man that hath this hope in him purifieth himself, even as he is pure." All of us are counting on this purifying to make us pure enough to receive eternal life. Psalm 12:6 says, "The words of the LORD are pure words: as sil-

ver tried in a furnace of earth, purified seven times." If one purifying is good enough for us, just one should be enough for God's word, but it has seven. This makes for a very accurate text, perfectly understandable and explaining every possible subject that we need to know.

Psalm 56:8 says, "Thou tellest my wanderings: put thou my tears into thy bottle: are they not in thy book?" In Webster's dictionary the word *tell* means to talk and record. The spoken word then is the same as the written word.

John 16:12 says, "the Spirit of truth is come, he will guide you into all truth: for he shall not speak of himself; but whatsoever he shall hear, that shall he speak." The Holy Spirit, who <u>is</u> God, speaks what he hears from God, the Father.

Hebrews 4:12-14 says, "For the word of God is quick, and powerful, and sharper than any twoedged sword, piercing even to the dividing asunder of soul and spirit, and of the joints and marrow, and is a discerner of the thoughts and intents of the heart." Jesus uses the scripture every time He answered Satan, because He knew that it is the word of God that pierces through Satan. "Neither is there any creature that is not manifest in his sight" (vs.13). The antecedent for the phrase "in <u>his</u> sight" is the Word of God, not God. So the Word of God is spoken of here as a <u>person</u>. Supporting this is Romans 9:17 which says, "the Scriptures raised Pharaoh up." Continuing on with vs.13, "but all things are naked and opened unto the eyes of him with whom we have to do." Once again, the phrase "eyes of <u>him</u>" also refers to "the word of God" in vs.12. Scripture is a person. "Seeing <u>then</u> that we have a great high priest, that is passed into the heavens, Jesus the Son of God, let us hold fast our profession" (vs.14). "Then" makes this verse which contains the phrase, "Jesus the Son of God" a reference also to "the word of God" in verse 12. So scripture is then equal to Jesus, who is the Incarnate Word of God (John 1:1-3). No wonder that Jesus said in Hebrews 13:5 "I will never leave thee, nor forsake thee." Scripture took his place. God the Father, God the Son, God the Holy Spirit *and* scripture are then interchangeable. 1 Pet 1:23 says, "by the word of God, which liveth and abideth for ever." The word of God, which is contained in scripture, is alive just as God the Father, the Holy Spirit and our Lord Jesus Christ are alive.

The Lord likes variety. One word is interchangeable with another word.

Philippians 2:9 says, "Wherefore God also hath highly exalted him, and given him a name which is above every name." The name of Jesus is above every name, but his word, scripture (KJV) is above even the name of Jesus.

Colossians 3:16 says, "Let the word of Christ dwell in you richly in all wisdom; teaching and admonishing one another in Psalm and hymns and spiritual songs, singing with grace in your hearts to the Lord." We are to "teach and admonish one another in Psalm." The Psalm are written words on paper. Then the "word of Christ" is a reference to scripture. We have to have a copy of scripture contains the words God wants us to have.

Something or someone has to be the final authority. Something or someone has to make a final decision and must be available to us right now. Either: Science, Greek Bible scholars, modern versions or the King James Bible.

1 Cor. 4:6 says, "That ye might learn in us not to think *of men* above that which is written, that no one of you be puffed up for one against another." We should not believe the speculations of scientists. Scripture is the final authority.

The name of God includes all the perfections of God; everything that God is, and which God has revealed Himself as having. In Ephesians 1:20,21 we read, "Christ... *is* ...Far above all principality, and power, and might, and dominion, and every name that is named, not only in this world, but also in that which is to come."

SEALED

"For the LORD hath poured out upon you the spirit of deep sleep, and hath closed your eyes: the prophets and your rulers, the seers hath he covered. And the vision of all is become unto you as the words of a book that is sealed, which men deliver to one that is learned, saying, Read this, I pray thee: and he saith, I cannot; for it is sealed..." (Isaiah 29:10,11)

The standard explanation is that we cannot understand parts of the Bible, because the book is sealed and this is the end of the discussion. To fully understand this verse there must be another verse to explain it, "...none (no verse) shall want her mate..." (Isaiah

34:16). The mate is in Rev. 22:10; Christ said, "...Seal not the sayings of the prophecy of this book: for <u>the time is at hand</u>". An objection is raised that we cannot go to Revelation because of verse 4:1, "After this...things which must be hereafter." The footnote says, after these things, meaning that from this point on, it is all in the future. All it is really saying is that after the discussion of the 7 churches, John is getting a preview of the future. Let's continue looking. Rev. 22:10 must also have a mate for the last part of the verse, "for the time is at hand." We find it at the beginning of Revelation in 1:3, "Blessed is he that readeth, and they that hear the words of this prophecy, and keep those things which are written therein: <u>for the time is at hand</u>." The time to use this book is now. There is no division in Rev. 4:1 between the present and the future.

So, by putting the two verses in Isaiah together, we can get a full and complete view of the truth. Some scriptures are <u>sealed</u> to scholars because of peer pressure and the fear of ridicule, and they are <u>not sealed,</u> but "...are plain to him that understandeth and right to them that find knowledge" (Proverbs 8:9). The Lord knew that Bible colleges would be started under the shadow and with the blessing of heliocentrism, evolution and modern versions, so He always has a scripture to keep his people from going in the wrong direction.

"Wherefore the Lord said, Forasmuch as this people draw near me with their mouth, and with their lips do honour me...and their fear toward me is taught by the precept of men... (Isaiah 29:13,14). The precepts of science have put fear into scholars.

"...Have not I written to thee excellent things in counsels and knowledge, That I might make thee know the certainty of the words of truth..." (Proverbs 22:21). Someone somewhere knows the actual meaning of each verse.

What God <u>said</u> is more important than the virgin birth, the deity of Christ or the blood atonement, since these were learned by believing the words found in the book. What God said, inspired and preserved is more important than Greek grammar, Hebrew sufformatives, older manuscripts, transmission of texts, reliable versions, conflated readings, "dynamic equivalents," archaeological findings, cursives, or uncials. Moses and Samuel heard the actual

236

words of God, the disciples were with Christ; we have to have true scripture that doesn't say the opposite of the truth.

TRANSLATORS

Isaiah 30:10 – "Which say to the seers...Prophesy not unto us right things, speak unto us smooth things, prophesy deceits." The committees writing modern versions knew they were giving misleading statements. Romans 1:18 (KJV) says "For the wrath of God is revealed from heaven against all ungodliness and unrighteousness of men, who hold the truth in unrighteousness." The NIV says "suppress the truth", because the reference was to them. They are actually holding it in their hands. They had the truth and changed it so that it was no longer the truth. Where else than modern versions does this apply in a better way? "Who changed the truth of God into a lie" (Romans 1:25). The King James in 2 Cor 2:17 has, "For we are not as many, which corrupt the word of God:..." NIV says, "...peddle the word of God for profit..." in order to cover up the sins of the NIV translators themselves, who are engaged in revising the Bible.

How serious is the problem of modern versions? Galatians 1:8,9 says, "But though we, or an angel from heaven, preach any other gospel unto you than that which we have preached unto you, let him be accursed. As we said before, so say I now again, If any man preach any other gospel unto to you than ye have received, let him be accursed." Any other gospel would be any modern version. The phrase "An angel from heaven" indicates ministers. Another phrase "any other gospel" has to be modern versions, since as we have seen, they have a different doctrine than the KJV. 1 Cor. 15:1,2 says, "...the gospel which I preached unto you, which also ye have received, and wherein ye stand. By which also ye are saved..." "The gospel which I preach" is obviously the one that does not diminish or deny the deity of Christ or corrupt the word of God. We are saved or our reward in heaven is greater using the KJV, not modern versions.

A KING

We know why:

Genesis 11:7 – "let us go down and there confound their language," to stop building the tower of Babel.

Acts 13:4 – "so they, being sent forth by the Holy Ghost," to spread the gospel

Gen. 1:2 – "the spirit moved" (See the First Second p.2)

Matthew 3:16 – "the Spirit of God descending," at the baptism of Jesus Christ.

John 16:13 – "the Spirit of truth, is come," to guide us to the truth.

Joel 2:29 – "In those days I will pour out of my spirit," who gave us our King James Bible.

But, we don't know why:

Acts 16:7 – "but the Spirit suffered them not."

Isaiah 42:4 – "and the isles shall wait for this law"

Jeremiah 31:10 – "Hear the word of the Lord, Oh ye nations, and declare it in the isles afar off"

"Where the word of a king is, there is power..." (Ecclesiastes 8:4). What does the phrase "a king" mean? This refers to an earthly king, King James of England. Far fetched? This means that the King James Bible is connected with an earthly king and has power. God's form of government is a monarchy. "And Simon Peter answered and said, Thou art the Christ" (Matt. 16:16). If the verse said "a Christ," this would refer to an earthly person instead of the Lord Jesus Christ. So, "a king" is an earthly king, not God. The King James Bible was translated and revised under the auspices of a king. The kings were all dethroned between 1790 and 1918 except the King of England. Modern versions are not connected with an earthly king and have no power.

"My son, fear thou the LORD and the king" (Proverbs 24:21). "Fear God. Honour the king" (1 Pet 2:17). The "king" is not Christ, but is an earthly king, and that is why "king" is not capitalized, but "God" is. And again, In England, there were many kings including Henry, John, Richard, and Thomas, but God waited until a "James" came along. The word "James" is the word "Jacob" (Greek: *Iakob*), who was a "prince" with God (Gen. 32:28). James is a Jewish name. "What advantage then hath the Jew? Much every way: chiefly, because that unto them (the literal physical Jews) were committed the oracles (will) of God." (Rom 3:1,2). The Jews had the advantage of Jesus Christ plus the words of truth. Jesus said, "for salvation is of the Jews" (John 4:22). These two verses link the English Bible, (translated under God's form of government- a monarchy) to the oracles or will of God. This is an historical truth. The God of scriptures is the God of history. History cannot be changed.

"Now when they...were forbidden of the Holy Ghost to preach the word in Asia, after they were come to Mysia, they assayed to go into Bithynia: but the Spirit suffered them not" (Acts 16:6,7). There were more cities and hence more people to bring the good news to in the east, so there must have been a strong reason for the Holy Spirit to direct them west. Without this explicit direction of the Holy Spirit, America would be in darkness and China would be a Christian nation!

"For our gospel came not unto you in word only, but also in power, and in the Holy Ghost and in much assurance; as ye know what manner of men we were among you for your sake" (1 Thess. 1:5). The gospel, the written word, came under the auspices of an earthly king. Regardless of whether an earthly king is a good ruler or not, God has given them power to rule.

God's power and glory are equal and interchangeable, "with power and great glory" (Matt. 24:30). The glory and power of the Lord always goes from east to west. "And, behold, the glory of the God of Israel came from the way of the east..." (Ezek 43:2). The gospel has to go from east to west just as the power of God does. "For I am not ashamed of the gospel of Christ: for it is the power of God...to the Jew first, and also to the Greek *Gentiles*" (Rom 1:16). The gospel goes from Israel westward to the British Isles. All nations between Israel and the British Isles will hear God's word and spread it to the west. Jeremiah 31:10 "Hear the word of the Lord, Oh ye nations, and declare it in the isles afar off." In the known world at that time, the British islands are as far away as possible from Israel.

"He hath not dealt so with any nation: and as for his judgments, they have not known them..." (Psalm 147:20). God has never worked with any nation as He will work with England (the British isles). The Holy Spirit directs Paul to take the word westward to the nation, later called England where king James (Jacob) will reign in the future. God's word, containing his words, is set for a future move to England. His word "runneth very swiftly" (vs.15). Just as the Holy Spirit has worked through prophets, priests and ordinary men such as the disciples, He now works through an earthly king, thus tying the Holy Scriptures to the earth. "At the same time spake the LORD by Isaiah the son of Amoz..."(Isa. 20:2). The Holy Spirit did not begin his work when Christ ascended back into heaven, work for 100 years and then quit. "When ye received the word of God which ye heard of us, ye received it not as the word of men, but as it is in truth, the word of God..."(1 Thess. 2:13). We should receive work of the committees that made the King James Bible and all Bibles leading up to it, as the exact words of God.

EAST

In scripture, if there is any hint of direction, it is always "from the east side unto the west side" (Ezekiel 48:8). Never west to east. "And, behold, the glory of the God of Israel came from the way of the east" (Ezek 43:2). "For as the lightning cometh out of the east, and shineth even unto the west (Mat 24:27). In them hath he set a tabernacle for the sun," (Psalm 19:4).

(Isaiah 4:6) "And there shall be a tabernacle for a shadow in the daytime from the heat, and for a place of refuge, and for a covert from storm and from rain." A covering shall be spread over all the glory. When the Lord sets up His Kingdom there will not be the cloud of glory just over the Tabernacle as in former days Exodus 40:34, but it will be spread over every dwelling place. (Exodus 40:34) "Then a cloud covered the tent of the congregation, and the glory of the LORD filled the tabernacle."

Absolute TIME is determined by Greenwich England; absolute LOCATION is determined by England (longitude); and absolute TEMPERATURE is determined in England (British thermal unit) and the ABSOLUTE TRUTH is also determined from England. The ONLY reason we are a Christian nation is because the Holy Spirit wanted absolute truth to be where absolute location and time would later be determined.

UNPARDONABLE

Nearly everyone thinks that Matthew12:31, 32, (also found in Mark 3:22-30,) is the unpardonable sin, which is the rejection of God the Father and God the Son, from which there is no hope of eternal life. We must let scripture help us interpret this verse. Isaiah 34:16 says "Seek ye out of the book of the Lord, and read: no one (no verse) of these shall fail, none shall want her mate." Every verse has another verse to explain and clarify it. This points us to consider Mark 3:29 which reads, "But he that shall blaspheme against the Holy Ghost hath never forgiveness, but is in danger of eternal damnation." Blaspheme means to injure the Holy Spirit by claiming the attributes of God and "to speak evil against." How have we claimed to be God? The Holy Spirit is the author of scripture. He has written the truth on our hearts and has guided us to God's word. We know the truth. We have seen and held the truth. When we choose a version other than the King James, we deny His work. The King James scripture will be in heaven. Modern versions will not be in heaven, only God's word.

Also, the footnote says, "there is no hope of salvation for him." Why, when it clearly states that he is only "in danger? Because, nearly everyone considers at least one modern version to be generally acceptable, leaving no other explanation.

"But ye have an unction from the Holy One, and ye know all things. I have not written unto you because ye know not the truth, but because ye know it..." (1 John 2:20,21). An "unction" is a very serious and most holy anointing or appointment for service and study (Exodus 30:36). We must be very careful in interpreting scripture and communicate with others before making final decisions. The Holy Spirit knew we would set aside the KJB, so He reminds us that we have it.

Psalm 147:4 says, "He telleth the number of the stars; he calleth them all by their names." The mate is - Isaiah 40:26, "...he calleth them all by names...not one faileth." Why is God telling us that he knows the name of each star? What's the point? There are billions times trillions of stars in the universe. God has <u>preserved</u> the exact, actual name of each star from the beginning until now.

The Bible only contains 810,697 words, so He surely has preserved the exact, actual words that He wants us to have.

HISTORY

The Bible is basically a history book, not a religious book. If you took the words "God," "Lord," and expressions like "the Most High" out, it would not even be called a religious book. The plan of salvation would take no more space than the book of Job. Most of it is history. God didn't use the word "Holy" until Genesis 53, and then referring to ground, not himself.

1 John 3:3 says, "And every man that hath this hope in him purifieth himself, even as he is pure." All of us are counting on this purifying to make us pure enough to receive eternal life. Psalm 12:6 says, "The words of the LORD are pure words: as silver tried in a furnace of earth, purified seven times." If one purifying is good enough for us, just one should be enough for God's word, but it has seven. This makes for a very accurate text, perfectly understandable and explaining every possible subject that we need to know.

Psalms 56:8 says, "Thou tellest my wanderings: put thou my tears into thy bottle: are they not in thy book?" The word *tell* means to talk and record. The spoken word is the same as the written word.

John 16:12 says, "the Spirit of truth is come, he will guide you into all truth..." The Holy Spirit, who is God, has guided mankind to the written word, containing the words God wants us to have, from the first century to the present.

INSPIRATION

Inspiration means an act of breathing in. In 2 Kings 18:13-19:37 is the story of Hezekiah and Isaiah trusting God to deliver them from Sennacherib. The same story is in Isaiah 37-38 with the additional information of Hezekiah's sickness and recovery. The work of inspiration in the giving of scripture took place twice. The second inspired writing was superior to the first even though it did not match the first. "When Moses came down from Mt. Sinai he had "two tables of testimony, tables of stone, written with the finger of God" (Exodus 31:18). Exodus 34:1 says, "And the Lord said unto Moses, Hew thee two tables of stone like unto the first: and I will write upon these tables the words that were in the first tables, which thou brakest." Hebrews 9:4 says, "Which had...the ark of the covenant...wherein was...the tables of the covenant." The second inspiration became the authority and was superior to the first.

When the Scriptures refer to the "scriptures" they never refer to the originals." Inspiration applies not only to the "originals" but also to copies and translations. All of the Old Testament quotations in the New Testament show the inspiration of a translation, since they are translated from Hebrew into Greek.

The word "inspiration" occurs in 2 Timothy 3:16. There must be a "mate" verse to support and explain in the verse we are working with. The word "inspire" is not in the Bible. The only other time the word "inspiration" occurs the in the Bible is Job 32:8 and here it is not dealing with scripture! Verse 8 says, "But there is a spirit in man: and the inspiration of the Almighty giveth them understanding." God "breathed in" to only one man: Adam. Yet the inspiration of the Almighty is applied to "them," to all men not just Adam. God breathed into Adam and it applied to all 6 billion of us. "The spirit of God hath made me, and the breath of the Almighty hath given me life" (Job 33:4), which supports Job 32:8.

The two verses are connected, but how? One is dealing with scripture and the other with men! The Almighty God is telling us that the miracle of inspiration applies not only to the initial giving of the Word of God to the writers of the original autographs, but to the divinely superintended preservation of a pure text to this day.

Job 33:16 says, "Then he openeth the ears of the men, and sealeth their instruction," What instruction? "To know wisdom and instruction; to perceive the words of understanding" (Prov 1:2), the KJ scripture. Because this copy was sealed, we have the absolute word of God uncorrupted! How do we know? "Being born again, not of corruptible seed, but of incorruptible, by the word of God..." (1 Peter 1:23). Only this one copy of scripture is the absolute incorruptible word of God.

A MORE SURE WORD

2 Peter 1:16-18 refers to the transfiguration. Continuing with 2 Pet 1:19 we read, "We have also a more sure word of prophecy; whereunto ye do well that ye take heed, as unto a light that shineth in a dark place, until the day dawn, and the day star arise in your hearts." The word "heed" means to pay special attention: to pay special attention to the fact that the King James scripture that we have is "a more sure word of prophecy." Than what? Than the transfiguration of Jesus that Peter and John saw face to face! How can this be true? We can read the scripture at any time; it is not limited to a one-time only event. During the transfiguration the "his face did shine as the sun" (Matt.17:2). Imagine the brightness of light from the sun if we were 30 or 40 feet away from it (assuming no heat). No darkness would be possible. We have the truth (a more sure word) in our hands, *if* we accept geocentricity. Why is that a requirement? The whole passage is talking about light; the rising sun causes the day to "dawn," not a spinning earth. Christ is the "day star." The truth (light) will come into our hearts and minds when we believe every word and extract the full meaning of every phrase and verse instead of the speculations of science.

SUPERIOR

The King James Bible is an inspired translation of the "original autographs." The King James Bible is those same autographs preserved up to today. The King James Bible is not only equal in authority and purity to the Masoretic and T.R. texts, it is superior to its source material. How?

1) It can be read. Most people cannot read Greek or Hebrew, but refer to the reference works of others.

2) It has chapter and verse divisions.

3) The KJV is in the universal language whereas the Greek and Hebrew are not. Chinese, Filipinos, Russians, and others have recognized the superiority of the KJV over even their own native Scriptures.

4) Masoretic text is not arranged in premillennial order and ends with 2 Chronicles. The Old Testament in the KJ ends with a warning about the 2nd Coming of Christ in Malachi.

5) The KJV is rhythmical and easy to memorize compared to the Greek and Hebrew.

6) The KJV is in a universal language. For instance, Chinese and Filipinos, who have a KJV along with a Bible in their native tongue, have recognized the superiority of the King James Bible over their native Scriptures.

We have the King James Scripture in English just like the Ethiopian had them in Coptic, Timothy had them in Hebrew and others had them in the Old Latin and the Old Syriac.

Only three things in the Scriptures are called "truth." Jesus Christ (John 14:6), the Holy Spirit (1 John 5:6) and the word of God itself. (John 17:17). Of the three, the Scriptures themselves are directly called "truth" more times than Jesus Christ or the Holy Spirit (Psalms 119:42, 151).

(Deu 30:10-12, 14 says, "If thou shalt hearken unto the voice of the LORD thy God, to keep his commandments and his statutes which are written in this book of the law…" "For this commandment which I command thee this day, it is not hidden from thee, neither is it far off. It is not in heaven, that thou shouldest say, Who shall go up for us to heaven, and bring it unto us, that we may hear it, and do it?" "But the word is very nigh unto thee, in thy mouth, and in thy heart, that thou mayest do it." The phrase "It is not in heaven" emphasizes the truth that the word of God, KJ scripture, is on the earth; we have to have it. It is in heaven "For ever, O LORD, thy word is settled in heaven" (Psalms 119:89), but we have a copy on the earth also. To get the full meaning we need both verses.

COMFORTLESS

John 14:16 says, "And I will pray the Father, and he shall give you another Comforter, that he may abide with you for ever." The phrase "another Comforter" implies that Christ, himself, is a comforter. The Holy Spirit is the "other Comforter" and he will be with mankind from Pentecost to the present time and forever. Verse 18 says, "I will not leave you comfortless: I will come to you." From this only, we see that Christ and the Holy Spirit are interchangeable.

"Nevertheless I tell you the truth; It is expedient for you that I go away: for if I go not away, the Comforter will not come unto you; but if I depart, I will send him unto you (John 16:7). Christ said he would never leave us, yet he said He would come to us, an apparent contraction. Obviously, the Comforter, the Holy Spirit takes his place. "Expedient" means necessary. Christ did not mind leaving, because he knew we would have just as much truth as the disciples had being face to face with Him.

John 16:13 says, "Howbeit when he, the Spirit of truth, is come, he will guide you into all truth..." Instead of being face to face with Christ, we are face to face with the "scripture of truth" (Daniel 10:21) under the guidance of the Holy Spirit. How long will we be guided by the Holy Spirit? He will abide with us "for ever" (John 14:26), not just 2 or 3 centuries, but by now, 20 centuries. What good would it do to "guide the blind" (Romans 2:19) only a short time and then let them fall? Continuing with verse 13 "and he will show you things to come." The Holy Spirit has revealed new truth in the Bible not just for the first 3 or 4 centuries since Pentecost, but in every century since then up to the present.

Not only will the Holy Spirit guide mankind forever, he will give the truth on everything we need to know: "But the Comforter, which is the Holy Ghost, whom the Father will send in my name, he shall teach you all things, and bring all things to your remembrance, whatsoever I have said unto you" (John 14:26). Christ left, but the Holy Spirit has led mankind to the "scripture of truth." Instead of talking to Christ face to face, we are "face to face" with scripture.

Jesus said he would "never leave us nor forsake us" (Heb. 13:5). Deut. 31:6 is the supporting verse. But he did leave. Jesus is the Word, "And the Word was made flesh, and dwelt among us..." (John 1:14). So, after Jesus ascended back to heaven, what happened to the "Word?" The "word of truth" (2 Cor. 6:7) became the "words of truth" (Ecc.12:10) which became the "scripture of truth" (Daniel10:21). With the Holy Spirit's guidance, mankind has always had the complete truth from Pentecost on to the present time. After all, Isaiah 40:8 says, "the word of our God shall stand for ever."

Every verse in the KJB is perfectly understandable and it all fits together perfect just like a crossword puzzle or a jigsaw puzzle.

COURT

2 Cor. 13:1 says, "...In the mouth of two or three witnesses shall every word be established." If a person is suing another person in a court case, every word spoken or written needs to be established. Every word is important. This should also be true on judgment day. However, churches use any and all versions. However, Matt. 4:4 says, "Man shall not live by bread alone, but by every word that proceedeth out of the mouth of God" and John 12:48 continues with, "He that rejecteth me, and receiveth not my words, hath one that judgeth him: the word that I have spoken, the same shall judge him in the last day." This refers to the scripture in the King James Bible. If every word is important between individuals, it is even more critical between man and God.

Every word? Every word includes all the words in scripture. "I rejoice at thy word, as one that findeth great spoil" (Psalm 119:162). How can we rejoice at "From the rising of the sun unto the going down of the same..." (Psalm 113:3) when we do not believe it?

The phrase '*the third time*' raises the issue of Paul's visits to Corinth. The first visit occurred in Acts 18:1, but what about the second? 2 Cor. 13:2 says, "I told you before, and foretell you, as if I were present, the second time; and being absent now I write to them..." The second visit was a letter not a personal visit! The letter Paul wrote is the same as his being there in person! What is the greater application of these verses?

Christ "the Word" (John 1:1) came in person the first time, but the Holy Spirit guided us "to all truth" (John 16:13) in the written word the second time! The written word (scripture) is interchangeable with the Living Word.

2 Cor. 13:1-3 – The point of these verses is the writing of a letter. This refers to the Holy Spirit guiding the writing of the KJ scripture. Very significant is the ending of 2 Corinthians. It is the only one of Paul's epistles which closes with a reference to "the

communion of the Holy Ghost" (verse 14). The Holy Spirit has communicated with the church through scripture.

DIFFERENCE

The Lord likes variety. He created many different kinds and shapes of living beings, minerals and etc. Humans are similar yet different. In view of this, lets consider God himself. He came in human form (Jesus) and then he came in a different form, the written form (KJV). To follow the Lord's leading we have to be flexible. If God can reveal Himself in the person of Jesus Christ, with all the limitations of being human, then He can reveal Himself in language and scripture (Peter Ruckman, www.kjv1611.org). Job 33:14 says, "For God speaketh once, yea twice, yet man perceiveth it not." Christ spoke and then the KJV has spoken.

COUNTENANCE

Mark 1:22 says, "he taught them as one that had authority." Jesus was the "Word" at his first coming, but will be a more powerful "Word of God" (Rev. 19:13) at the 2nd coming. Rev. 1:16 says, "and out of his mouth went a sharp twoedged sword: and his countenance was as the sun shineth in his strength." Comparing the countenance of Christ with the sun refers to "Sun of righteousness arise" (Malachi 4:2). If the Sun doesn't really move (rise) then the Son hasn't risen; in other words, geocentricity. The sharp twoedged sword is the word. The spoken word becomes the written word to a far greater extent than ever before. The written word now has the authority that rightfully belongs to it. The outcome of this is that the church will then learn the high cost of rejecting geocentricity.

A list of good books on the subject of the preservation of scripture:

How to Teach the "Original" Greek by Peter Ruckman: written harshly, I focus on what he says about the verses. Bible Believers Press, PO Box 7135, Pensacola FL 32534. www.kjv1611.org

Ruckman's Bible References by Peter Ruckman. (I've read

about 20 of his books.)

The Answer Book by Samuel Gipp - Question 1, 28 and 31.

An Understandable History of the Bible by Rev. Samuel Gipp, pages 45, 108, 161, 170.

New Age Bible Versions by G. A. Riplinger. www.avpublications.com.

Which Bible Is God's Word? by Gail Riplinger, pages 55, 56, 89, and 116.

The Language of the King James Bible by Gail Riplinger

Things That Are Different Are Not the Same by Mickey Carter

Let's Weigh the Evidence by Barry Burton, pages 20-27

The Battle for Christian Music by Tim Fisher

Comparing the written word to the Living Word: one example – the Lord can make you to understand:

(Proverbs 28:5) Evil men understand not judgment: but <u>they that seek the LORD understand all things</u>.

The Word can make you to understand:

(Psalm 119:100) <u>I understand</u> more than the ancients, <u>because I keep thy precepts</u>.

Both God and the word are: righteous, precious, truth, eternal, light and in 150 other ways in his book.

Chapter 7

THE UNIVERSE IS RELATIVELY SMALL

We know what that secular scientists believe the universe is large and continually getting larger, but what is God's opinion? After all, "Heaven and earth shall pass away: but my words shall not pass away" (Luke 21:33). We are going to live forever with God and His word, not the secular world. His Word will be on the eternal new earth. Let us then heed what it has to say about the size of the universe.

Is the universe expanding? "Thus saith God the Lord, he that created the heavens, and stretched them out; he that spread forth the earth..." (Isaiah 42:5). God stretched out the heavens only during the first second of creation. "The carpenter stretched out his rule..." (Isaiah 44:13). It is not still stretching out. "It is he (God)... that stretcheth out the heavens as a curtain, and spreadeth them out as a tent to dwell in" (Isaiah 40:22). Curtains stretch but tents do not. These verses do not indicate continuous expansion as secular science teaches us. In looking at Psalm 136:6 we find, "To him that stretched out the earth." The earth was stretched out, yet has a limited size and is not expanding. As the earth is not expanding, so neither is the heavens. Whoever heard of a continually expanding tent? Scripture tells us that "...thou hadst formed the earth and the world (universe) (Psalm 90:2). God formed the earth and it is the same size as it was in the beginning. The universe, also, is the same size as it was in the beginning.

2 Peter 3:7, says "But the heavens and the earth, which are now, by the same word are kept in store" refers to the universe just after Noah's flood. Webster's dictionary says that "store" means to preserve it exactly as it was when first stored. Therefore, at least, the universe is the same size as it was right after the flood, approximately 4400 years ago.

THE RAINBOW FACTOR

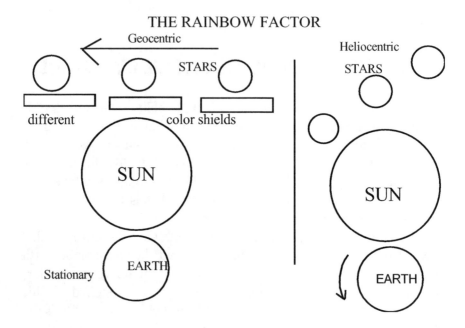

Why should the rainbow be involved with "the brightness" in the firmament? Different colors are in front of various stars and make them appear to have different amounts of brightness, because there is "another glory of the stars: for one star differeth from another star in glory" (1 Cor. 15:41). Individual stars that appear to have different amounts brightness, and therefore different distances from the earth, are simply behind different colors of the rainbow, which affects their brightness. The stars with different degrees of brightness may be side by side or relatively close together.

Psalm 123:2 says, "Behold, as the eyes of servants look unto the hand of their master...so our eyes wait upon the Lord our God..." Servants" watch for the slightest sign of their masters will. When looking into a telescope with your eye and seeing 2 stars side by side, one star being bright and the other dim, it is assumed that the bright star is much closer than the other. In reality, the bright star is sealed perhaps with a yellow color and the other covered with violet. The stars actually are side by side. God's word must be considered before decisions are made. Our eyes should look to all of scripture to see if there is anything that applies to what we see.

Lets refer again to Isaiah 34:16, "none (no verse) shall want her mate." Every verse in scripture is supported or made clear by another verse. Isaiah 25:7 says, "...and the veil that is spread over all nations." A veil is the same as a shield. There definitely is something between the stars and the earth.

Since we are dealing with God and not man the logical result is many wild theories. That is the theme is this book. Supporting this is Psalm 47:9; "for the shields of the earth belong unto God." The "shields" are the different colors of the rainbow and God has told us that "his truth" is our "shield" (Psalm 91:4).

These "shields" are between us and the stars. How do we know this? 1Samuel 17:7 says, "and one bearing a shield went before him." A shield is always between men or objects. The phrase, "For the Lord God is a sun and shield" (Psalm 84:11), shows that the shield is in the same location as the sun; between the earth and the stars. We must rely on scripture to know the distance to the stars. In John 20:14, Mary did not recognize Jesus even through she looked right at him. Only when Jesus caused her to see clearly (vs.16), did she know him. Only with God's word in scripture, can we see the truth clearly.

Creationist always wins debates with evolutionist on all subjects ranging from fossils, rock strata, bombardier beetle, mutations, forming of the grand canyon, heat of the earth, radiometric dating, flow of nickel from rivers into the ocean, receding rate of Niagara Falls, the second law of thermodynamics and etc. Then they go along with the secular evolutionists on the size of the universe, slowing the total truth of God's word.

If our churches believe in creation, (a young earth) instead of evolution (the earth is billions of years old), this is still not a totally solid foundation. John Morris is president of the Institute for Creation Research, PO Box 2667, El Cajon, CA 92021 (www.icr.org). In his newsletter of August 2001, he writes about an "Impact" article, Starlight and Time, which addresses "a serious" problem in creation. Light travels at 186,000 per second. Getting distant starlight from stars billions of light years away to the earth in only 6000 years (let alone one day) is, and I quote, "we cannot yet claim to have a possible solution to the distant starlight problem." It is a "longstanding creationist problem." Continuing with a creation magazine, Technical Journal, Answers in Genesis, Volume 15(2) 2001 (PO Box 6302, Acacia Ridge D.C., Qld. 4110. Australia), it addresses the problem of distant starlight by suggesting several solutions: the decreasing speed of light, time dilation in outer space, zero is not zero and finally, calculated and observed time.

Our church is based on this type of reasoning! The church must have a "sure foundation" (Isaiah 28:16) based on Christ, who is the Word, which is scripture.

The Lord knew that mankind would believe the stars are billions of light years away, so Daniel 7:25 says, "and (mankind would) think to change times and laws." If it is pointed out that "And he (God) changeth the times and the seasons" (Daniel 2:21), this verse applies to Genesis 1:14 "and let them be for signs, and for seasons, and for days, and years." The final solution must be going back to the absolute truth in the King James Bible, which is openly geocentric. R.G. Elmendorf wrote in the Biblical Astronomer pamphlet, "The philosophical consequences of the geocentric/heliocentric controversy are plain enough that if the earth is not fixed on center stage of the universe, then life on earth and man himself are essentially meaningless."

1 Cor. 5:6 says, "Know ye not that a little leaven leaveneth the whole lump?" I feel we have to know the size of the universe to demolish completely evolution with its billions of years. We should consider all of scripture to see if there is anything that applies to what we see.

How does light from stars, traveling 186,000 miles per second, get to the earth in one day, much less 6000 years, when the stars are millions of light years away? God's word takes precedence over the decreasing speed of light or time dilation or observation. The King James scripture tells us "all things" (John 14:26): the earth is 6000 years old, the sun orbits a stationary earth, and the universe is relatively small, but still to big to "be measured" (Jer. 31:37).

Let's just see what scripture does tell us. "And I saw another mighty angel come down from heaven, clothed with a cloud: and a rainbow was upon his head, and his face was as it were the sun, and his feet as pillars of fire (Rev 10:1). "And there appeared a great wonder in heaven; a woman clothed with the sun, and the moon under her feet, and upon her head a crown of twelve stars" Rev 12:1.

Putting it all together, the proper order from the end of the universe inward is: the stars, the rainbow, the sun, the moon and the earth at the center.

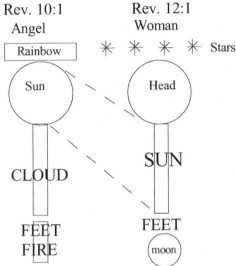

Also ruling out a large universe is the rainbow. "And I saw another mighty angel come down from heaven, clothed with a cloud; and a rainbow was upon his head, and his face was as it were the sun, and his feet as pillars of fire" (Rev. 10:1). The rainbow, being upon his head, is above his face (which represents the sun). This shows that rainbows exist beyond the sun as well as in the atmosphere and between the earth and the sun. Rev. 12:1 shows the location of the stars to be above the sun: "And there appeared a great wonder in heaven; a woman clothed with the sun, and the moon under her feet, and upon her head a crown of twelve stars." The stars and the rainbow are both above the sun, and the stars are located in the rainbow.

Is there any support for this theory? Yes! Every verse is explained or supported and made complete by another verse (Isaiah 34:16). "[God] sealeth up the stars" (Job 9:7). Why? To physically surrounded each star with a different color of the rainbow. "It is to the glory of God to conceal a thing" (Proverbs 25:2). Only scripture can tell us the distance to the stars. The author of scripture, the Holy Spirit, has a very real purpose in writing this. Secular scientists looking through a telescope should stop and check the words of God before making a final decision on the distance to the stars. Only by checking God's words can be know some things. (See also "The First Second" page 4.)

If the space represented by the woman's head is the distance from the sun to the rainbow and stars at the end of the universe. If the woman's head represented the actual size of the sun, which 886,000 miles in diameter, then the sun would be at the very end of the universe. "Midst means the middle of the firmament. Joshua 10:13 says, "the sun stood still in the midst of heaven..." This shows the sun to be in the middle of the universe. If the sun were located at the angel's knees, there would be support for a larger universe, but it isn't. Physicists should get the viewpoint of scripture before making decisions.

Looking now at the last part of the verse, "and his feet as pillars of fire" (Rev. 10:1). "Fire" refers to Rev. 20:14, which says, "And death and hell were cast into the lake of fire..." The lake of fire is in the center of the earth, so "fire" in verse one refers to the earth.

The drawing below condenses considerably the size of the universe from that which we hear about from the news media.

Psalm 74:17 says, "Thou hast set all the borders of the earth." It isn't "borders of the "sun, moon and stars" (universe). "Borders" keep things inside. The earth cannot move through the borders, so the earth does not orbit the sun. This also effectively rules out the earth spinning on its axis daily.

(Genesis 1:16) "And God made two great lights; the greater light to rule the day, and the lesser light to rule the night: he made the stars also." The greater light is the sun and the lesser light is the moon. Could the sun be the greater light and rule the day in an arbitrary reference frame, such as the Andromeda Galaxy? It would be invisible without an extremely powerful telescope! The sun can be the greater light only within the solar system. The moon is even more restricted. It can fulfill its God-given role in creation as the lesser light, only from the reference frame centered on the earth, which shows the earth is the center of the universe. By including "the stars," he was showing that the sun and moon were the greater and lesser lights for the entire universe, which limits its size to a relatively small universe. "The moon and stars to rule by night" (Psalms 136:9) shows that the light from the stars reached the earth just ten minutes later than the light from the moon. The truth must fit in with scripture, "...the worlds were

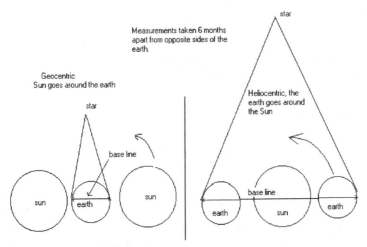

framed by the word of God..." (Heb 11:3). What God does always agrees with what he says.

Both the greater and lesser lights were set in the firmament (v.17). Either both orbit the earth, or neither one does.

Since science now admits to being unable to prove that this is not the absolute reference frame for creation, we can accept the Bible's clear statements as absolutely true and not "figurative."

The moon can be the lesser light only in a relatively small universe, because if the sun were the frame of reference, the moon couldn't be seen. The universe cannot be expanding because it has been framed and frames do not expand," the worlds (universe) were framed by the word of God." (Heb 11:3).

FRAME

Next, what does scripture say about a "frame"? "God...set me upon a very high mountain, by which was as the frame of a city on

256

the south" (Ezekiel 40:2). Ezekiel is on a mountain looking at the city. The mountain is the frame of reference. In the case of the universe, the earth is the frame of reference. The law heliocentrism demands that we assign a near-infinite distance to the stars, which is the opposite from what God is telling us.

"For the stars of heaven and the constellations thereof shall not give their light" (Isaiah 13:10). Constellations are dark. In reference to what? The earth! Constellations, groups of stars or galaxies, are part of the solar system with the earth at the center.

Who has caused the confusion about the size of the universe? "Shall the throne of iniquity have fellowship with thee, which frameth mischief by a law?" (Psalm 94:20) The throne of iniquity is Satan's, "I will exalt my throne" (Isaiah 14:13). Satan has caused the secular world to believe that frames expand. The size of the universe is very important.

Isaiah 29:16 says, "Surely your turning of things upside down shall be esteemed as the potter's clay...or shall the thing framed say of him that framed it." This verse explains Isaiah 24:1, which refers to a one-time rotation of the earth (See Joshua's Long Day in the Revolving Heaven article). This one time rotation of the earth is in relation to the firmament or universe. So God framed the universe and frames do not expand. The universe cannot be expanding.

Hebrews 11:3 says, "the worlds were framed by the word of God..." Every "jot" (Matt. 5:18), letter and word are important. To even begin to understand the firmament there must be, at least, many other worlds or universes. So, if God framed the "worlds", he certainly framed the "world" or our universe. The footnote says that "worlds" mean "ages." This is incorrect because ages refer to time in eternity, but Rev. 10:6 says there will be "Time no longer." Time or ages does not exist in eternity. The other three scriptures that have the word "ages" refer to time in this 7000+ year period on the earth. So "worlds" means worlds or universes, not ages.

(From the Biblical Astronomer, No. 83, p.19)

In one particular Internet discussion group, Dr. Arnold Sikkema, a physicist from the university of Florida states "...no physicist I know says that the earth in any absolute sense travels around the sun. (Sikkema A., "Absolute Frame," REFNET Geocentricity Study Group, 24 Jul 1997). Science today does not claim that there is an absolute reference frame in which the earth is moving." Scripture looks at things "In the earth's reference frame." "Frame of reference" means context or the place where a person is located. The Bible deals with truth and absolutes, so "geocentric" implications cannot apply to an arbitrary frame of reference.

"...God...set me upon a very high mountain, by which was as the frame of a city on the south." (Ezek 40:2). The frame of reference is Ezekiel on a mountain looking at the city, which shows that a "frame of reference" is a Biblical term.

The earth is the moral center of all that God has done in the universe. It was here that God became a man and later died for the sins of the world. The same God that came to the moral center is the same God that created the physical universe, which shows that the earth really is in the center of the universe. There is no need for the earth to spin in a corner.

DEEP

We read that God said "Let there be light" and that "He formed the light", but the "deep" was simply placed in existence because God is omnipresent. Webster's dictionary says that "deep" has 2 or 3 meanings and one meaning is that "deep means the plenum". The deep is an attribute of God, a characteristic of God, or, more precisely, an extension of His omnipresence. God is a plenum.

God's word says that the deep is rotating. Proverbs 8:27 says, "When he set a compass upon the face of the depth." The definition of "deep" in Webster's Dictionary includes the word "depth" and the definition of "depth" has the word "deep". They can be used interchangeably. One synonym for deep is the firmament. The synonym for "compass" is "to make the circuit of." The deep is part of the firmament and rotates in a circle orbiting a stationary earth as the firmament does. Daniel 7:9 says, "...his wheels as burning fire". The "deep" and the firmament are 2 wheels that are revolving around the earth. The firmament revolves around the earth daily and the "deep" spins around the universe at 10^{23} times per second or "as burning fire," electromagnetism. However,

Job38:30 says, "...the face of the deep is frozen." If the deep is like fire, how can it be frozen? It cannot be freezing cold. This shows that the Planck particles in the deep are frozen solid as a unit and cannot react to any movement within them. Each particle in the "deep" cannot move in relationship to any other particle, but the deep, the rim, spins as a solid unit around the center of the universe, the earth. Starlight cannot shine outward to penetrate the deep, but only inward to the earth.

The opposite is true of Planck particles in the firmament where the particles react instantly to movement within them. The phrase "the brightness of the firmament" (Daniel 12:3) refers to the Planck particles in the firmament. "Brightness" is a synonym for light. Since light is present, the Planck particles move in relationship to every other particle, letting objects in the firmament travel through the firmament without any friction, unaware of anything there.

Finally, there is the open firmament of heaven, the atmosphere, where planes fly.

The firmament is composed of 3 parts. The open firmament, which does not rotate; the firmament which rotates around the stationary earth daily; and the deep which spins at 10^{23} times per second around the universe.

But, where is the location of the deep?

"Thou art the anointed cherub that covereth; and I have set thee so: thou wast upon the holy mountain of God; thou hast walked up and down in the midst of the stones of fire" (Ezekiel 28:14). Lucifier was the anointed cherub in heaven with God. The holy mountain is heaven, so the "stones of fire" must be next to heaven, except that the deep is part of the firmament and the waters are above the firmament. (Gen.1:7)

Job 20:26 says, "darkness shall be hid in his secret places." There are two places for darkness, in the center of the earth and covering the deep at the end of the universe. "Where is the way where light dwelleth? and as for darkness, where is the place thereof, That thou shouldest take it to the bound thereof, and that thou shouldest know the paths to the house thereof?" (Job 38:19,20). "Way" indicates that light dwells everywhere and moves whereas darkness is referred to as a place and a "place" does not move. The darkness is bound and cannot move, rotate, expand or shrink. Since darkness covers the deep, the deep cannot expand or shrink, but it rotates under the darkness as a solid unit. The universe is a house and a house does not expand unless it is blown up. Nothing but God himself penetrates the deep.

"Light" in Genesis 1:3 refers to the atomic structure, Planck particles and electromagnetism. One definition of light in the ninth edition of Webster's Dictionary is "electromagnetism." The universe cannot be expanding for the reason that "the light is short because of darkness" (Job 17:12). Electromagnetism (light) can go only to the edge of the darkness, which covers the deep. But Planck particles are electromagnetism and are in the deep. This shows that the particles have a different function in the deep than in the firmament. "He setteth an end to darkness"(Job 28:3). Where at? The darkness extends only from the waters above the firmament inward the width of the deep. Why? The Planck particles behave different in the deep than in the firmament. They move only in the firmament. The darkness, which doesn't move, covers the deep that is spinning around the universe.

The stars are in the 2nd heaven next to the deep. The Planck particles move out of the way as stars go in their own individual orbits while at the same time the middle firmament enclosing the sun, moon and stars revolves around the earth.

At the other end of the firmament, the earth, the deep covers the atoms of the earth. Note Psalm 104:5,6: "Who laid the foundations of the earth, that it should not be removed forever. Thou coveredst it (foundations) with the deep as with a garment:.." Think of the foundations as the atoms of the earth. Then visualize the deep covering those atoms (the foundation) like a garment. The deep (electromagnetism) controls the atoms or foundation of the earth and stabilizes it.

Connect Genesis 49:25 to this: "...and by the Almighty who shall bless thee with blessings of heaven above, blessings of the deep that lieth under..." What blessing do we receive from the deep? The deep limits the size of the universe. As scientific creationism and geocentricity are true, so also is a non-expanding universe. God's words answer every criticism the secular world has.

TOLD US ALL THINGS

The complete truth includes the size of the universe. John 14:2 "In my Father's house are many mansions: if it were not so, I would have told you." "House" has no meaning to us unless it is a physical place, the universe. The word "mansions" is found only here in scripture, so to find the mate verse that explains this verse, lets go to the phrase, "if it were not so." [Isaiah 34:16 says, Seek ye out the book of the Lord, and read: no one of these shall fail, none shall want her mate.] The phrase "not so" is found 38 times in scripture. Of all of these verses, only one has anything to do with revealing the complete truth, and that is found in 1 Sam 20:2, "And he said unto him, God forbid; thou shalt not die: behold, my father will do nothing either great or small, but that he will show it me: and why should my father hide this thing from me? it *is* not *so*." Notice also the words, great or small. "Great," is the subject under discussion, the size of the universe. If Saul would hide nothing from Jonathan, why should God hide the size of the universe from us? The size is of extreme importance. "Howbeit when he, the Spirit of truth, is come, he will guide you into all truth" (John 16:13), which includes the size of the universe. Creationists have a strong defense in every subject concerning the age of the earth except the size of the universe. The Lord Jesus Christ also, has told us the complete truth concerning the universe.

"It is to the glory of God to conceal a thing" (Proverbs 25:2). The sealing of the stars conceal the distance to the stars. Only by reading God's words in scripture, can we know the size of the universe. Acts 20:20 says, "And how I kept back nothing that was profitable unto you..." Knowing the size of the universe completely destroys the last shred of support for evolution.

Psalm 82:5 says, "...all the foundations of the earth are out of course." This is talking about what we believe, "...but the righteous is an everlasting foundation." The basic foundational beliefs of the world are: (1) that the earth is billions of years old, (2) that the earth is spinning on its axis daily, (3) and that the stars are billions of light years away from the earth. All of these are wrong. The King James scripture says (1) the earth is 6000 years old (2) is stationary and (3) the farthest stars are one-half light day away.

GOD'S OFFER

"Ask thee a sign of the Lord, thy God, ask it either in the depth, or in the height above" (Isaiah 7:11). The word 'sign' has about a dozen meanings two of which apply here: (1) it refers to motion, or (2) something indicating the existence of a thing. The words 'depth' and 'height' refers to heaven and earth as Proverbs 25:3 says, "The heaven for height, and the earth for depth." God *actually* offered to explain that the firmament was extremely dense and that it revolves around the earth daily with the universe embedded in it.

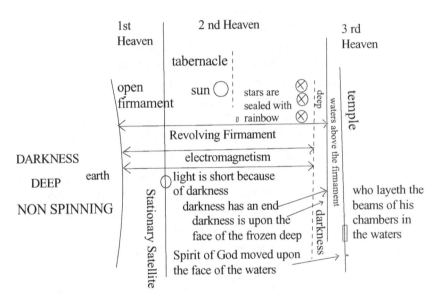

SIZE

Did God tell us the size of the universe? He has told us about ordinary things such as: "Now also when I am old, and grayheaded O God" (Psalms 71:18). This is common knowledge and accepted by everyone. Surely, He has told us the ballpark size of the universe.

Nothing bothers those who believe in a young earth when refuting evolution except a large universe.

Psalm 47:9 says, "for the shields of the earth belong unto God." The "shields" are the different colors of the rainbow. These "shields" are between us and the stars. How do we know this?

1 Samuel 17:7 says, "and one bearing a shield went before him." A shield is always between men or objects. Psalms 84:11 says, "For the Lord God is a sun and shield." As the sun is between the earth and the stars, so are the shields. We must rely on scripture to know the distance to the stars. In John 20:14, Mary did not recognize Jesus even through she looked right at him. Only when Jesus caused her to see clearly (vs.16), did she know him. Only with God's word in scripture, can we see the truth clearly.

Creationists always win debates with evolutionist on all subjects ranging from fossils, rock strata, bombardier beetle, mutations, forming of the grand canyon, heat of the earth, radiometric dating, flow of nickel from rivers into the ocean, receding rate of Niagara Falls, the second law of thermodynamics and etc. Then they go along with the secular evolutionists on the size of the universe, slowing the total truth of God's word.

If our churches believe in creation, (a young earth) instead of evolution (the earth is billions of years old); this is still not a totally solid foundation. John Morris is president of the Institute for Creation Research, PO Box 2667, El Cajon, CA 92021 (www.icr.org). In his newsletter of August 2001, he writes about an "Impact" article, Starlight and Time, which addresses "a serious" problem in creation. Light travels at 186,000 per second. Getting distant starlight from stars billions of light years away to the earth in 6000 years (let alone one day) is, and I quote, "we cannot yet claim to have a possible solution to the distant starlight problem." It is a "longstanding creationist problem." Continuing with a creation magazine, *Technical Journal*, Answers in Genesis, Volume 15(2) 2001 (PO Box 6302, Acacia Ridge D.C., Qld. 4110, Australia), it addresses the problem of distant starlight by suggesting several solutions: the decreasing speed of light, time dilation in outer space, zero is not zero and finally, calculated and observed time.

Our church is based on this type of reasoning! The church must have a 'sure foundation' (Isaiah 28:16) based on Christ, who is the Word, which includes the words that God wants us to have. Churches that believe in theistic evolution are not even close to the truth on this question, but for churches that accept a young earth of about 6000 years, this is still not close enough.

The Lord knew that mankind would believe the stars are billions of light years away, so Daniel 7:25 says, "and (mankind would) think to change times and laws." The only way to reconcile to an extremely large universe with a young universe is to change the time. This verse eliminates that possibility. John 16:12 says, "I (Jesus) have many things to say unto you..." One of the many things Christ had to tell us is the relatively small size of the universe.

I mentioned on the cover page that following what the scriptures actually say, stretches the limit of understanding, but we are dealing with God and not man.

Each day of creation week ended with the phrase, "evening and morning." Why didn't it say, "morning and evening"? The Holy Spirit had the words written in this order for a special purpose. He wanted to tell us something of major importance. Gen. 1:4 says, "And the evening and the morning were the first day." When referring to ordinary days after creation week there are only two verses that contain the phrase "morning and evening" or "evening and morning" and also have the word "day" included. One is 1 Samuel 17:16: "And the Philistine drew near morning and evening, and presented himself forty days" and the other: "And when they had appointed him a day...from morning till evening," Acts 28:23. Both say "morning and evening," just the opposite of creation week. This emphasizes that the starting time of each day during creation week was the beginning of the evening. Gods' purpose in writing scripture this way was to tell us the relatively small size of the universe!

"And that he would shew thee the secrets of wisdom, that they are double to that which is!...canst thou by searching find out God? canst thou find out the Almighty unto perfection? It is as high as heaven..." (Job 11:6,7,8). This applies to the physical universe, the stars, because, "Search the scriptures (God)" (John 5:39) is spiritual and can be done. Looking at the stars through a telescope will not give the complete truth. Conclusions drawn from this only will not be perfect. Scripture must be considered. "Thus saith the Lord...which giveth...the ordinances of the moon and of the stars for a light by night...If those ordinances depart from before me, saith the Lord, then the seed of Israel also shall cease from being a nation... " (Jeremiah 31:35,6). These ordinances or laws, apply to equally to both the moon and the stars. Light from the moon was not created in transit. Neither was the light from the stars created in transit! Light from the stars still arrived on schedule in the evening of the fourth day.

Science is wonderful, but the only reliable clue to the distance of the stars is in scripture. Science will never be able to penetrate the different color shields. Proverbs 22:12 says, "The eyes of the LORD preserve knowledge..." We are dependent on God and his word to know the distance to the stars. Isaiah 11:3 says, "And shall make him of quick understanding in the fear of the LORD: and he shall not judge after the sight of his eyes." Christ will judge with the word of God, not with his eyes. We should do the same now.

This gives a fairly accurate measurement of the distance to the stars. Am I then measuring heaven? Jeremiah 31:37 says, "...If the heavens above can be measured, and the foundations of the earth searched out beneath, I will cast off all the seed of Israel..." This will never happen. The heavens will not be measured. The solution is that the "third heaven" (2 Cor. 12:2) is beyond the stars. The stars are set "in the firmament of the heaven" (Gen. 1:17), the second heaven, not the third heaven.

Psalms 148:1,3 says, "Praise ye the LORD. Praise ye the LORD from the heavens: praise him in the heights. Praise ye him, sun and moon: praise him, all ye stars of light." The capital case "LORD" means Jehovah. The LORD himself is speaking, and is telling us that the universe is both natural and supernatural. Otherwise, the sun, moon and stars would not praise God. Science is wonderful, but the only reliable clue to the distance of the stars is in scripture. Science will never be able to penetrate the different color shields. Proverbs 22:12 says, "The eyes of the LORD preserve knowledge..." We are dependent on God and his word to know the distance to the stars.

1 Cor. 5:6 says, "Know ye not that a little leaven leaveneth the whole lump?" I feel we have to know the size of the universe to completely demolish evolution with its billions of light years. "Wisdom (from God) strengtheneth the wise more than ten mighty (scientific) men which are in the city" (Ecc. 7:19).

[From the Spring 2002 issue of the Biblical Astronomer: NASA spacecraft Pioneer 10 and 11, which were launched in 1972, are mysteriously slowing down. They seem to be pulled back to the sun by an unknown force. Scientists are now considering the possibility that the law of gravity may be different than originally thought. Duncan Steel, a space scientist at Salford University in Manchester, England, says even such a weak force could have huge effects on a cosmic distance scale. "It...raises the question of whether we know enough about the law of gravity."] At the present time, this gives very good support to a relatively small universe.

Chapter 8

Evidence – Earth's annual orbit

Is the earth spinning daily on its axis or not? If it is spinning daily, it must also be orbiting the sun yearly.

When walking in a rain that is coming straight down, a person must tilt his umbrella forward into the rain to keep from getting wet. This is called an aberration. The earth's alleged orbit around the sun should exhibit a similar aberration of starlight. This is illustrated on the front cover, where the starlight hits the lens at point 1 and by the time the light travels down to tube to the eyepiece at point 2, the telescope has moved to the left the right amount to overcome the motion of the telescope from right to left. A second item that could cause an aberration is called the Fresnell drag. The sun has an aether-field coupled to it that sweeps past the earth once a year. This field could be the sun's light or magnetic or gravitational field. It drags starlight with it causing the aberration.

In the 1870s a fundamental experiment, now called "Airy's failure," measured the alleged 67,000 miles per hour orbital speed of the earth around the sun. The result gave a speed of zero. Later experiments with greatly improved accuracy have given the same result.

Airy's Failure

Because of the earth's speed about the sun, a telescope must be tipped slightly ahead of the actual position of a star to get the starlight going down the axis of the tube so that the star can be seen. The telescope was then filled with water which slowed down the speed of light to 77% of its speed in air. Starlight will then take longer to go through the telescope and the telescope will have to be tilted in order to see the star. The result was that the angle of the telescope did not change! The water-filled telescope had to be kept in the same position as the empty telescope to see the star. This implied that the star was moving and not the earth. If the water filled telescope had to be tilted more than the empty telescope to see the star, it would mean that the earth was moving around the

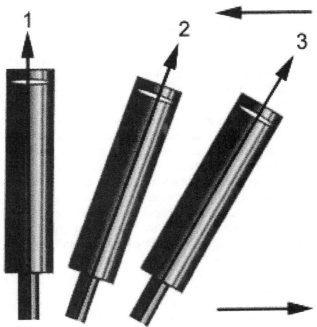

sun. So "Airy's failure" failed to prove that the earth revolves about the sun.

In each case, in the above figure, the arrow points to where the star appears to be in the sky. In the first figure, the star is straight up. It represents the case where the star is overhead and the earth does not orbit the sun. The second case shows where the star appears if the star's true position is overhead but the earth goes around the sun at 30 km/sec, represented by the arrow at bottom right. The third telescope points to where the star would appear if the earth goes around the sun and the telescope is completely filled with water. The telescope has to be pointed further in front of the star because it takes longer for the light to travel down the telescope tube. Nevertheless, Airy observed the same direction for both the empty and the water-filled telescope, namely, direction 2.

If, however, the star sweeps by the earth, as indicated by the arrow at upper right, then both the air filled telescope (2) and the water filled telescope (3) will point in the same direction (2). Airy expected his "failure" because of the results of the Fresnell drag experiment, indicating that the water drags the light with it.

See also: Michelson-Morley and Michelson-Gale experiments.

Evidence - Pattern

At the 2002 International Conference on Creationism, I talked with Fred Willson, who spoke on Fibonacci sequences. His work was written up in ICR's *Impact* #354 in December 2002.

Even though he wrote the *Impact* article, he had never seen it in print. He looked at it and noticed that, under ratio, the top "8:21" for the earth was put there by someone else. He had left it blank. Then he looked at the article, "ICR Skirts Geocentricity Again," by Gerardus Bouw, Ph.D., (4527 Wetzel Ave., Cleveland, OH 44109) and said that he had suspected that his article indicated geocentricity. As of Nov. '03, he personally likes what Dr. Bouw did with his *Impact* article #354, but hasn't taken the time to peruse it in detail.

The Institute for Creation Research does not believe in geocentricity. The *Impact* article, "Shapes, Numbers, Patterns, and the Divine Proportion in God's Creation," may be found at http://www.icr.org/pubs/imp/imp-354.htm. The article by Gerardus Bouw "ICR Skirts Geocentricity Again," is located on the web at www.geocentricity.com/bibast/no103/icr_fibronacci.pdf.

I was having a hard time understanding Fred Willson's *Impact* #354 article until I put in the following:

	(Percent)	(Theoretical)
Neptune		62,000
Uranus	50	31,000
Saturn	33	10,333
Jupiter	39	4,133
Asteroids	37	1,550
Mars	38	596
Earth	<u>61</u>	366
Venus	40	277
Mercury	31	87

(The 50% is found by dividing 31,000 by the number above it 62,000 and so on down the list)

Gordon Bane
911 Van Buren
Hugoton, KS 67951
gbane@pld.com

Below are reproductions of the two aforementioned papers.

"VITAL ARTICLES ON SCIENCE/CREATION"

impact

December 2002

Impact #354

SHAPES, NUMBERS, PATTERNS, AND THE DIVINE PROPORTION IN GOD'S CREATION

by Fred Willson, M.S.*

In God's creation, there exists a "Divine Proportion" that is exhibited in a multitude of shapes, numbers, and patterns whose relationship can only be the result of the omnipotent, good, and all-wise God of Scripture. This Divine Proportion—existing in the smallest to the largest parts, in living and also in non-living things—reveals the awesome handiwork of God and His interest in beauty, function, and order.

I will first begin with shapes, then discuss how a numbering pattern and a ratio (the Divine Proportion) are an inherent part of these shapes and patterns and are ubiquitous throughout creation.

Let's begin with a shape with which we are all familiar. It is the spiral commonly seen in shells. By taking a careful look at that spiral (the chambered nautilus is probably the clearest example) you will observe that as it gets larger, it retains its identical form. Since the body of the organism grows in the path of a spiral that is equiangular and logarithmic, its form never changes. The beauty of this form is commonly called the "golden spiral."

This spiral is visible in things as diverse as: hurricanes, spiral seeds, the cochlea of the human ear, ram's horn, sea-horse tail, growing fern leaves, DNA molecule, waves breaking on the beach, tornados, galaxies, the tail of a comet as it winds around the sun, whirlpools, seed patterns of sunflowers, daisies, dandelions, and in the construction of the ears of most mammals.

This spiral follows a precise mathematical pattern. We will first look at this spiral in sunflowers. By looking carefully at a sunflower you will observe two sets of spirals (rows of seeds or florets) spiraling in opposite directions. When these spiral rows are counted in each direction, you will discover that in the overwhelming majority of the cases that their numbers, depending upon the size of the flower, will be of the following ratio:

if small, 34 and 55; if medium 55 and 89; if large 89 and 144

---

* Fred Willson is ICR's Extension Specialist in Science Education.

These numbers are part of the Fibonacci numbering sequence, a pattern discovered around A.D. 1200 by Leonardo Pisa (historically known as Fibonacci). *Each succeeding number is the sum of the two preceding numbers.* The sequence of these numbers is 1,2,3,5,8,13,21,34,55,89,144,233, ad infinitum. This numbering pattern reveals itself in various ways throughout all of nature, as we shall see.

When the smaller number of this pattern is divided into the larger number adjacent to it, the ratio will always be approximately 1.618; if the larger one adjacent to it divides the smaller number, the ratio will be very close to 0.618. *This ratio is only true for this set of numbers.* This ratio has been called historically the Divine Proportion or Golden Ratio. This ratio has served mankind in three ways: it provides beauty, function, and reveals how marvelous God is.

Beauty

Why did Phideas, the Greek sculptor, and many others in ancient Greece and Egypt use this ratio in designing their works of art? Because this ratio has been found to be remarkably pleasing to the human eye, it produces what is called a Golden Rectangle. If the short side of the rectangle is 1, the long side will be 1.618. This rectangular shape was used in the designing of the Parthenon in Greece and as the basic shape for many of their numerous pictures, vases, doorways, windows, statues, etc. It appears in the Great Pyramid of Egypt. The United Nations building is a golden rectangle. Many of the things you use are (approximately) patterned after the golden rectangle—credit cards, playing cards, postcards, light switch plates, writing pads, 3-by-5 and 5-by-8 cards, etc.[1]

Artists such as Leonardo da Vinci, Van Gogh, Vermeer, John Singer Sargent, Monet, Whistler, Renoir, and others employed the golden proportion in their works. They would "take a blank easel and divide it into areas based on the golden proportions to determine the placement of horizons, trees, and so on."[2] Why the golden proportion? Art forms can be either of static or dynamic symmetry. In static symmetry the lines have definite measurements whereas in dynamic symmetry it is the proportioning of the areas that is given emphasis. It implies "growth, power, movement. It gives animation and *life* to an artist's work . . . rather than the effect of stillness and quiet"[3] of static symmetry. This is the appeal of the golden proportion.

Another area of great interest is the occurrence of Fibonacci numbers in the spiral arrangement of leaves around a plant's stem (called phyllotaxis). This spiral pattern is observed by viewing the stem from directly above, and noting the arc of the stem form one leaf base to the next, and the fraction of the stem circumference which is inscribed. In each case the numbers are Fibonacci numbers. Examples: In an elm the arc is 1/2 the circumference; in beech and hazel, 1/3; apricot, oak, 2/5; in pear and poplar, 3/8; in almond and pussy willow, 5/13; and in some pines either 5/21 or 13/34. Why did God arrange them this way? This pattern assures that each leaf will receive its maximum exposure to sunlight and air without shading or crowding other leaves.

Not only do we discover this pattern in leaf arrangements, but it is also found in the arrangement of flower petals. Examples: a lily has 3 petals, yellow violet 5, delphinium 8, mayweed 13, aster 21, pyrethrum 34, helenium 55, and michaelmas daisy 89. With such a great variety of spiral ratios in leaf and petal arrangement, no one has any reason to get bored with God's creation.

When we realize that the information to produce these spirals and numbers in living things is stored in the DNA, should we then be surprised to find that the DNA molecule is 21 angstroms in width and the length of one full turn in its spiral is 34 angstroms, both Fibonacci numbers? The DNA molecule is literally one long stack of golden rectangles.[4]

Let's look into the area of very small and very large things. In the world of atoms there are four fundamental asymmetries (structure of atomic nuclei, distribution of fission fragments, distribution of numbers of isotopes, and the distribution of emitted particles), and it is significant that "the numerical values of all of these asymmetries are equal approximately to the 'golden ratio,' and that the number forming these values are sometimes Fibonacci or 'near' Fibonacci numbers."[5] In changing states of a quantity of hydrogen atoms, as the atoms gain and lose radiant energy at succeeding energy levels, the changing proportion of the histories of the atomic electrons form Fibonacci numbers.[6]

In the area of very large phenomena when the time period of each planet's revolution around the sun is compared in round numbers to the one adjacent to it, their fractions are Fibonacci numbers! Beginning with Neptune[7] and moving inward toward the sun, the ratios are 1/2, 1/3, 2/5, 3/8, 5/13, 8/21, 13/34. These are the same as the spiral arrangement of leaves on plants!

Revolution of the planets in days and their correlation to Fibonacci numbers and spiral arrangement of leaves on plants[8]

	Observed	(theoretical)		Ratio	Plants
(Pluto)	90,000			(2:3 Neptune)	—
Neptune	60,193	62,000			—
Uranus	30,688	31,000		1:2	Elm
Saturn	10,760	10,333		1:3	Beech
Jupiter	4,332	4,133		2:5	Apricot
Asteroids	1200-2000	1,550		3:8	Pear
Mars	687	596		5:13	Almond
Earth	**365**	**366**	8/13	**8:21**	—
Venus	**225**	**277**	13/21	**8:21**	Pine
Mercury	88	87		13:34	Pine

There are creationists who have theorized that some cosmic force, probably in relation to the day of Noah's flood, altered the solar system, especially from Venus to the asteroid belt. This may account for the only significant theoretical adjustments in the chart: Mars (687 to 596), and Venus (225 to 277); the rest are very close to reality. Even with these two adjustments, the correlation of the Fibonacci pattern to the periodic times of the planets is far more than just a chance arrangement. It is one more example of God's marvelous mathematical arrangement of His creation. The fact that it is not perfect reveals that although Adam's sin affected the whole creation (Romans 8:22), yet God in His goodness has not allowed sin to overcome all the marks of His great handiwork (Psalm 19:1).

A most interesting divergence in the chart is that of the Earth. As the next planet in the series after Mars, its number should be 8:21, but it isn't. This number "skips" over Earth and connects to Venus. Even with this divergence we find that the Earth's period compared to Mars and Venus are Fibonacci numbers (8/13, 13/21). It is my opinion that this anomaly is evidence of God's showing the uniqueness of planet Earth in relationship to the whole cosmos. It also accomplishes another fact, for this "anomaly" shatters the big bang and nebular hypothesis, for if all the planets formed from a whirling cloud of dust and atoms, this feature would not be present. To think that the times of revolution of the planets around the sun correlates with the arrangement of leaves around stems on plants is also an amazing phenomena.

These shapes, numbers, spirals, and the divine proportion are ubiquitous in their presence throughout all of creation. They are found in living and nonliving phenomena. Their symmetry, beauty, and mathematical preciseness are evident in every aspect of nature. Although absolute perfection is not found in all of these (due to the effects of Adam' sin), their very presence virtually everywhere and in everything argues against their having occurred by blind chance or evolutionary processes. The only rational conclusion is that the Creator of the universe is a personal, intelligent Being, who created these things as a visible fingerprint of His invisible, yet personal existence. This great, wise, powerful, creative, and sovereign God of creation is the One revealed in the Bible, of whom it can be said, "Great things doeth He, which we cannot comprehend" (Job 37:5). He is worthy of worship. And what is His name? The Lord Jesus Christ. "Thou art worthy, O Lord, to receive glory and honour and power: for thou hast created all things, and for thy pleasure they are and were created" (Revelation 4:11).

References

1. Trudi Hammel Garland, *Fascinating Fibonaccis*, Dale Seymour Publications, 1987, p. 19. Available: www.bbhomeschoolcatalog.com or 800/260-5461.
2. Ibid., pp. 34, 36.
3. Garth E. Runion, *The Golden Section,* Dale Seymour Publications, Palo Alto, CA. 1990, pp. 84–85.
4. Marl Wahl, *A Mathematical Mystery Tour,* Zephry Press, Tucson, AZ. 1988, p. 128.
5. J. Wlodarski, "The Golden Ratio and the Fibonacci Numbers in the World of Atoms," *Fibonacci Quarterly*, December 1963, p. 61.
6. H. E. Huntley, "Fibonacci and the Atom," *Fibonacci Quarterly*, December 1969, pp. 523–524.
7. There is still controversy as to whether Pluto is a real planet. Whether or not it is, its distance from Neptune is still a Fibonacci ratio, even if in the opposite direction.
8. Marcius Willson, *The Fourth Reader of the School and Family,* Harper & Brothers, Publishers, New York, 1860, p. 216.

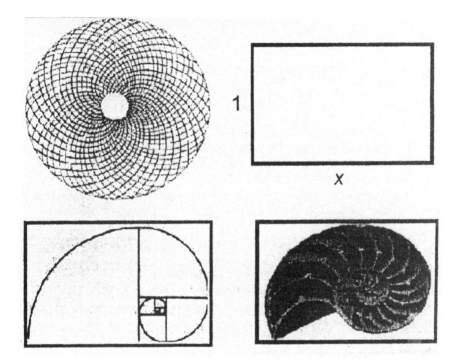

1

X

ICR SKIRTS GEOCENTRICITY AGAIN

December's issue of *Impact* from the Institute for Creation Research was devoted to an article by Fred Wilson on the mathematical
patterns found in nature.[1] In particular, the article describes a mathematical sequence called a *Fibonacci Series*. The series is created by
taking the numbers one and two and then forming the next number in
the sequence by adding the previous two together. The series runs:

$$1, 2, 3, 5, 8, 13, 21, 34, 55, 89, 144, 233, 377, ...$$

When the larger of an adjacent pair of numbers is divided, the larger by
the smaller, the ratio is usually close to 1.618. This ratio is called the
Golden Ratio. It turns out that rectangles, whose sides satisfy this ratio,
are pleasing to the eye. The ratio of these pages is about 1.55. The
Greeks used the *golden rectangle* in the design of their temples. The
ark of the covenant was 2.5 cubits long and 1.5 cubits wide, which is a
ratio of 1.6767. The altar for sacrifices was 3 cubits high, by 5 long and
wide. The list of ratios for the above list is:

$$2, 1.5, 1.667, 1.6, 1.625, 1.615, 1.619, 1.618, 1.618, 1.618, 1.618, 1.618$$

More difficult to see is the pattern in flowers. A flower like the
sunflower will have two sets of spirals spiraling in opposite directions.
(Each spiral is made of tiny flowers which yield the sunflower seeds.)
Counting in each direction, one finds that the number of tiny flowers or
seeds, depending upon the size of the flower, will number a follows: if
the flower is small, 34 and 55, if medium 55 and 89, and if large 89 and
144. These form what is called a *golden spiral*.

Mr. Wilson does a very nice job of showing the broad scope under
which the golden spiral, rectangle, and ratio occur. The reader is encouraged to get a copy or check for it at ICR's web site.

The most interesting part of the article from our perspective is the
Fibonacci sequences for the planetary periods. Wilson's table could be
clearer by using years in stead of days and by showing more intermediate values, but his table served the purposes of his article just fine. The
following table includes intermediate values, including one for the asteroids. We selected the largest asteroid, Ceres, for the period of an
asteroid. Wilson's 1550 days gives a period of 4.24 years and actually

---

[1] Wilson, F., 2002. "Shapes, Numbers, Patterns, and the Divine Proportion in God's
Creation," *Impact*, no. 354, December.

does not match the ratios as well as the Ceres period, which is representative of the largest asteroids.

FIBONACCI RATIOS FOR THE PLANETS

Planet	Period (years)	Observed Period Ratio	Expected Fibonacci Ratio	Expected Fibonacci Value	Best-fit Observed Ratio	Best-fit Observed Value
Pluto	248.43	---	---	---	---	---
Neptune	164.78	**1.51**	3:2	1.50	3:2	**1.50**
Uranus	84.02	**1.96**	2:1	2.00	2:1	**2.00**
Saturn	29.46	**2.85**	3:1	3.00	3:1	**3.00**
Jupiter	11.86	**2.48**	5:2	2.50	5:2	**2.50**
Asteroids	4.60	**2.58**	8:3	2.67	8:3	**2.67**
Mars	1.88	**2.45**	13:5	2.60	13:5	**2.60**
Earth	1.00	**1.88**	21:8	2.63	*13:8*	**1.63**
Venus	0.62	**1.61**	34:13	2.62	*21:13*	**1.63**
Mercury	0.24	**2.58**	55:21	2.62	55:21	**2.62**

In the table, the first column lists the name of the planet. The second column gives its orbital period, its "year," in earth years. The third column is computed by dividing the period of the planet on the line above by the period of the planet on that line, giving the observed ratio of the periods.[2] For instance, the value of 1.51 for Neptune is computed by dividing the period of Pluto, 248.42 years, by Neptune's period of 164.78 years. The fourth column gives the Fibonacci ratio that is theoretically expected to give to the value in column three, only expressed as a fraction of two integers. The Fibonacci ratios start with Uranus as 2 to 1 (2:1, read as "two to one"). Neptune's Fibonacci ratio is in the opposite direction of the planets interior to Uranus. The ratio of 5:2 for Jupiter is derived by adding the 2 from Uranus and the 3 from Saturn to give the 5. The 2 is found by adding the 1 from Uranus to the 1 from Saturn. The fifth column is the ratio in column 4 divided out to two decimal places. In other words, the 2.60 for Mars is computed by the division 13/5. Columns four and five are theoretical, that is, computed, values derived from Uranus's starting value. The values in column five are to be compared with those in column three. Note that the computed values fail to match the observed ones, for earth and Venus.

---

[2] Wilson presents the inverse, but the only effect is to swap the numbers in the ratio, that is, the 3:1 for Saturn becomes 1:3. It makes no difference in the analysis or the results. It's just a personal preference, I'd rather work with numbers like 3 instead of 0.33333....

The sixth and seventh columns give the best-fit observed match to column three, given the expected sequence. Thus I have left the ratio for Mercury the same as expected (55:21) whereas Wilson changes it to 34:13. Since both ratios evaluate to 2.62, there is no way to tell which is "correct." Columns six and seven, then, express what is actually *observed*, not what is wished for, while keeping the values in columns three and four, where appropriate.

The table is not the same as appeared in the *Impact* article. In the original article, the period of Mars was changed from 1.88 years to 1.63 years, and that of Venus was changed from 0.62 year to 0.76 year. Also, Wilson's article had the planetary periods in days, but whether days or years, it makes no difference to the ratios since they are unitless. Using the adjusted periods for Mars and Venus vastly improves the results in column six, for then the ratio for both earth and Venus becomes 21:8. The ratio for Mars was kept the same by adjusting the period for the asteroids from 4.60 to 4.24 years.

We find that the earth and Venus are oddballs, neither fitting the expected Fibonacci series. Thus we should compare column three with column seven; the observed ratio of the period, to the observed ratio value.

The table at left shows the error, that is, the difference between the observed Fibonacci ratio (O), and the computed value (C). The subcolumn labeled "Theory" is the difference between columns 5 and 3 in the first table. "Best fit" is column 7 minus column 5. The last column is the Theory column less the Best fit column of this table. By far, the largest discrepancy is for the earth. At -0.26, its magnitude is 1.7 times larger than the errors for Saturn and Mars, both of which are near "asteroid belts," meaning that their periods may not be representative of the mass distribution in that are.

ERROR ANALYSIS		
	O-C	Theory minus
Planet	Theory	Best fit	Best fit
Pluto	---	---	---
Neptune	-0.01	-0.01	0.00
Uranus	0.04	0.04	0.00
Saturn	0.15	0.15	0.00
Jupiter	0.02	0.02	0.00
Asteroids	0.09	0.09	0.00
Mars	0.15	0.15	0.00
Earth	0.75	-0.26	1.00
Venus	1.00	0.00	1.00
Mercury	0.04	0.03	0.00

All things considered, the fit for the outer planets (Pluto through Mars) is good, as is Mercury's. The only problems planets, as clearly

Planet	Observed Period	Wilson's Period	Observed Period Ratio	Wilson's Period Ratio	Expected Fibonacci Ratio	Wilson's Fibonacci Ratio	Our Corrected Ratio	Expected Fibonacci Value	Wilson's Fibonacci Value	Our Corrected Value
Pluto	248.43	248.43								
Neptune	164.78	164.78	1.51	1.51	3:2	3:2	3:2	1.50	1.50	1.50
Uranus	84.02	84.02	1.96	1.96	2:1	2:1	2:1	2.00	2.00	2.00
Saturn	29.46	29.46	2.85	2.85	3:1	3:1	3:1	3.00	3.00	3.00
Jupiter	11.86	11.86	2.48	2.48	5:2	5:2	5:2	2.50	2.50	2.50
Asteroids	4.60	4.24	2.58	2.80	8:3	8:3	8:3	2.67	2.67	2.67
Mars	1.88	1.63	2.45	2.60	13:5	13:5	13:5	2.60	2.60	2.60
Earth	1.00	1.00	1.88	1.63	21:8	21:8	13:8	2.63	2.63	1.63
Venus	0.62	0.76	1.61	1.32	34:13	21:8	21:13	2.62	2.63	1.52
Mercury	0.24	0.24	2.58	3.17	55:21	34:13	55:21	2.62	2.62	2.62

DETAILED COMPARISON WITH WILSON'S ANALYSIS

seen in the last column of this table, are earth and Venus. (Do not be alarmed that earth's value is not 1.01. This is because of rounding errors. The underlying values in the spreadsheets shown carried more than three significant digits.)

The table at left is a comparison of our results with Wilson's. The last three columns should fit the observed values in column 4.

After making his adjustments to the periods of the asteroids, Mars, and Venus, Wilson writes: "It is my opinion that this anomaly is evidence of God's showing the uniqueness of planet Earth in relationship to the whole cosmos." We can take that a step further and point out that if he is correct, then it shows that the earth is not a planet. Wilson correctly notes that this would not be expected if the solar system formed by the commonly accepted Nebular Hypothesis. The solar system had to be created, for if it came about by chance, the Fibonacci series would apply to the earth, too.

But our analysis did not fudge the planetary periods to force a fit to the Fibonacci ratios. We found that without altering the periods of Mars, the asteroids, and Venus, only two objects are affected, Venus and earth. Although Wilson's fudging gives him a nice recovery of the ratios, isolating the difference to earth, the process itself is questionable. Wilson does not go into a detailed defense for his action other than to wave his hands saying that some creationists have postulated that an "unknown cosmic force" altered the solar system about or at the time of Noah's flood. But that is nothing more than a creationist version of Velikovskyism. The "unknown cosmic force" is proposed because the actions postulated cannot naturally occur. It is possible that miraculous events at the time of the flood may have moved the planets around, but as there was no need for God to do so to create the flood, and as there is no mention of such events in Scripture, it seems pointless to invent a superficial miracle to explain what may or may not be a true pattern in planetary periods.

Elsewhere we have noted the special place that Venus holds in the creation.[3] Venus is the only planet identified with the Deity. In particular, Venus, the morning star, is identified with the Lord Jesus Christ in Revelation 22:16, "I Jesus have sent mine angel to testify unto you these things in the churches. I am the root and the offspring of David, *and* the bright and morning star." Though it may be tempting to adopt Wilson's analysis and say, "See! The earth is not a planet," there is sufficient evidence for that without this rather circumstantial datum. But if both Venus and earth hold a special place, as indicated in both analyses (in his table, Wilson highlighted both their rows in green), we should not be upset. Both earth and Venus have a special place in Scripture; earth because God created it for man, to dwell there and to enjoy God's glory and grace; and Venus as a type of the Scripture–as a light shining in darkness and heralding the morning, and as the herald of the Lord Jesus as he will return to establish a righteous and everlasting kingdom on earth. What Wilson has stumbled upon is not so much that the earth is special, but that the Scripture is special; for no other solar system objects, except the sun and moon, are singled out specially in Scripture. Earth and Venus are distinct in the Fibonacci series because they are distinct in Scripture: the earth because it is in a special state, i.e. stationary, in creation, and Venus because it is a type of the Lord Jesus, both the word of God (Mk. 7:13) and the Word of God (Rev. 19:13).